C·O·R·R·A·L·S

FOR HANDLING BEEF CATTLE

By Robert Borg, Regional Engineer

with assistance from

Region 3 Beef Facilities Group;
Stuart Tucker, Ken Williamson,
Trevor Yurchak, Ken Ziegler and Dale ZoBell

reviewed by

Engineering Services Branch
Richard Smith, Regional Engineer, Airdrie
Wayne Winchell, Regional Engineer, Barrhead
Dennis Darby, Farm Structures Engineer, Lethbridge
Temple Grandin, Colorado State University

Published by:
Alberta Agriculture, Food and Rural Development
Publishing Branch
7000 - 113 Street
Edmonton, Alberta
Canada T6H 5T6

Production Editor: David Orey
Graphic Designer: Wendy Luedtke

ISBN 0-7732-6126-5

First printing 1993
Second printing 1994
Third printing 1996 01 2.5M

• • • • • • • • • Acknowledgements • • • • • • • •

Credit is due to many sources for the written material and drawings contained in this publication.

The chapters on cattle behavior are based on extensive research papers presented by Temple Grandin, Colorado State University, Department of Animal Sciences and Grandin Livestock Handling Systems Inc.

Ideas for the various components and layouts were derived from sources such as: the Canada Plan Service, Saskatchewan Agriculture, Midwest Plan Service (MWPS) from the United States, the Western Regional Agricultural Engineering Service (WRAES) in Washington, and Alberta Agriculture, Food and Rural Development.

The corral costs were calculated using a Lotus 1-2-3 spreadsheet developed by Dennis Darby, farm structures engineer, Alberta Agriculture, Food and Rural Development, Lethbridge.

The blind box chute and corral layout 11 were developed by Trevor Jones, beef specialist, Alberta Agriculture Food and Rural Development, Fairview.

Special thanks to Christine Corbett for her contribution to the publication.

C·O·N·T·E·N·T·S

I·N·T·R·O·D·U·C·T·I·O·N

Good cattle handling systems make work easy for limited manpower operations and confine cattle in a hazard free environment.

Well designed corrals will:
- reduce handling time and operator requirements
- increase operator safety
- minimize animal injury and stress during treatment and handling operations.

The operation of any cattle facility depends on cattle behavior, corral design and the skill and technique of the handler. The number of cattle to be handled, the number of handlers and the time available, all affect the appropriate corral design. This publication looks at cattle behavior, shows how to design cattle handling corrals, and gives instructions on how to build gates, pens, fences and working areas.

A complete cattle handling facility will allow you to:
- gather • direct the flow • hold • sort • position

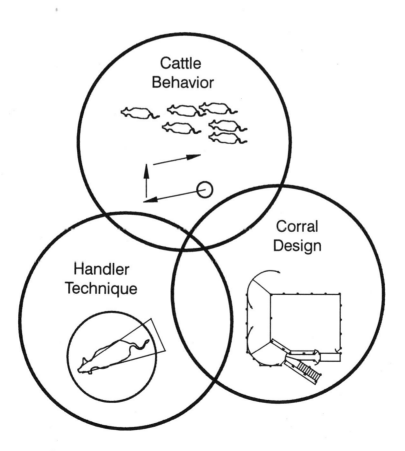

Figure 1. The cattle handling equation

C A T T L E
B·E·H·A·V·I·O·R

▶ **EFFECTS OF STRESS ON CATTLE**

- Reduced weight gain
- Poor reproductive performance
- Reduced ability to fight disease

> *Temple Grandin says, "Handling practices can be less stressful to the animals and safer for the handler if one understands the behavioral characteristics of livestock."*

Genetics
Breed differences mean some cattle are more excitable. Recognize this while handling cattle.

Individual differences
Each animal is an individual and has a different reaction to stress.

Past experience
Animals have long memories. If they have been handled roughly in the past, they will be more stressed and difficult to handle in the future. Choice is a factor in stress - feedlot cattle who will freely investigate a coat hanging on a fence will balk when forced to walk past the same coat hanging on a chute or flapping in the breeze.

Familiarity with the environment
New pens and facilities are stressful. Let the cattle get used to the corrals. Cattle also show signs of stress when they are isolated. A single animal left alone in a crowding pen or working chute will try to rejoin its herdmates and may charge the handler.

▶ **REPRODUCTION**
Rough handling during artificial insemination (AI) can raise body temperatures and lower conception rates. High body temperature at the time of insemination increases the risk of early embryonic death. Excitement before insemination depresses secretion of hormones that stimulate contractions of the reproductive tract that move sperm to the site of ovum fertilization. Use a dark box to hold cows. You can hold the wildest cow with minimum distress.

▶ **DISEASE**
There is evidence that stress due to rough handling can affect cattle's immune response - they are more susceptable to disease.

▶ **VISION**
Cattle have excellent wide angle vision, in excess of 300 degrees, due to the position of their eyes. Cattle can see behind themselves without turning their heads. Ruminants do have depth perception, but they have difficulty perceiving depth at ground level while they are moving with their heads raised. To see depth at the ground the cow has to lower its head, perhaps explaining why cattle balk at shadows or distractions at ground level.

► UNDERSTANDING THE FLIGHT ZONE

The flight zone is the animal's personal space. If you move inside the flight zone the animal will move away. When you back off, the animal will stop moving. The size of the flight zone depends on wildness or tameness of the cattle, angle of handler approach and state of excitement of the cattle. Work at the edge of the flight zone at an angle 45° to 60° behind an animal's shoulder. The cattle will circle away from you. The flight zone radius may be five to 25 feet for feedlot cattle and 300 feet for range cattle. If you are behind the point of balance the animal moves forward. If you are ahead of the point of balance the animal retreats.

A technique that works well with cattle that are moving is not to approach cattle directly, but to work close to the point of balance, moving back and forth on a line parallel to the direction the animal is travelling.

Figure 2. The flight zone

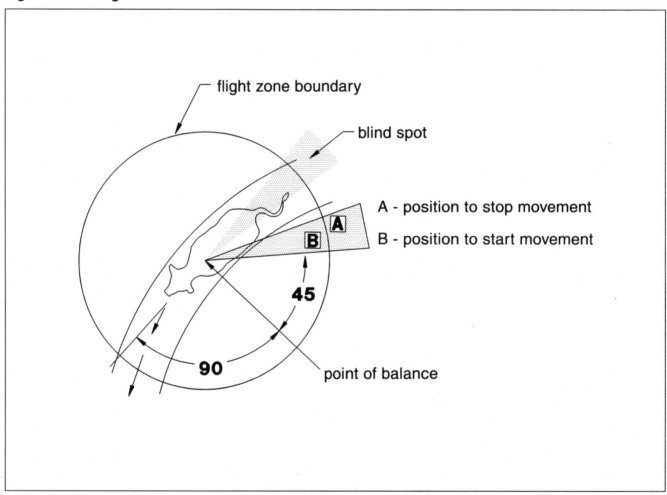

flight zone boundary

blind spot

A - position to stop movement

B - position to start movement

45

90

point of balance

Figure 3. Increased flight zone

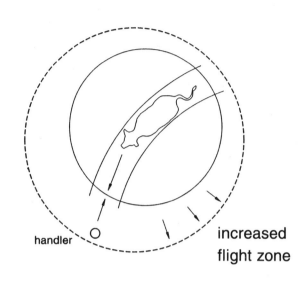

- The flight zone increases when you approach head on.

- The flight zone increases when the animals are excited.

handler

increased flight zone

Figure 4. Decreased flight zone

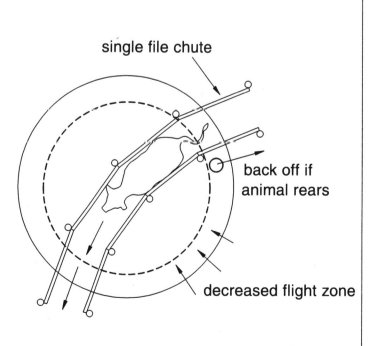

- Flight zone decreases when animal is in a single file chute.

- Flight zone decreases for a cow passing by you.

- Penetration deeply into the flight zone of a cow in an alley may cause panic. If the animal rears in the chute, back off.

single file chute

back off if animal rears

decreased flight zone

▶ CURVED CHUTES

Curved working chutes prevent the animal from seeing the truck, squeeze chute and people until it is almost in the truck or squeeze. A curved chute takes advantage of the animal's natural circling behavior. As you enter a pen the animals will form a circle around you and face you. As you move through the pen they will circle around you.

A catwalk along the inside of the chute will force the handler to stand in the best position for moving the animal and will let the animal circle away from the handler. Never have a catwalk overhead.

▶ HERD INSTINCT

Cattle follow the leader. They are motivated to maintain visual contact with each other. Each animal should be able to see others ahead of it. Make single file chutes at least 20 feet long, 30 to 50 feet for larger facilities. Don't force an animal in a single file chute unless it has a place to go. If the cow balks it will continue balking.

Blocking gates in a chute need to be "see through" so cattle can see the animals ahead. If the cow sees a dead-end it will balk.

Handle small groups in crowding pens, eight to 10, instead of 20. The cattle need room to turn. Use the cattle following behavior to fill up the chute. Wait until the single file chute to the squeeze is almost empty before refilling. The crowd gate is used to follow the cattle, not to shove up against them. If a lone animal refuses to move, release it and bring it back with another group.

An animal left alone in a crowding pen will become agitated and may attempt to jump the fence to rejoin its herdmates.

▶ RESPONSE TO LIGHT

Uniform lighting is important. Cattle avoid shadows. Striped shadows and contrasting patterns will cause balking.

Cattle in the dark will move towards the light. If you are loading at night, use a frosted light to shine into the truck. Avoid glare in their faces.

Livestock tend to balk if they have to look into the sun. Face your loading chute and squeeze north-south for summer handling.

Cattle may refuse to enter a dark, indoor working chute from a bright, outside crowding pen. Extend the chute outside the building or cover the crowding area.

▶ RESPONSE TO MOVEMENT

Cattle balk at moving or flapping objects. Use solid sides for the construction of crowding pens, single file chutes and loading chutes. Stand back from the headgate so that the cattle can not see you.

H A N D L E R
T·E·C·H·N·I·Q·U·E

Temple Grandin, noting methods used by Bud Williams (U.S.A.) and Ron Kilgour (New Zealand), outlines some principles of moving groups of cattle.

• Quiet gathering of cattle from the pasture is the key - no whistling, hollering, loud noises or running. The cattle become quieter and easier to handle.

• Don't chase cattle from the rear of the group. This puts you in their blind spot, they will turn and look at you (unless they are scared and fleeing from you).

Figure 5. Moving groups on pasture

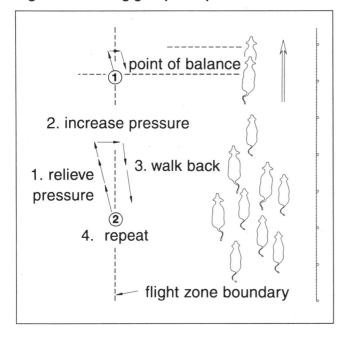

▶ **SINGLE HANDLER**
 Use the handler 2 position:
1. As the herd moves walk forward at an angle that relieves the pressure on the herd's flight zone.
2. As the animals slow down, increase the pressure on the flight zone by walking straight towards the cattle.
3. As the herd speeds up, turn and walk back opposite the direction of travel. A slight angle will increase the pressure on the flight zone.
4. Repeat the pattern to maintain movement. The pattern is important, walking parallel to the herd will split the herd.

Like a car, the group must be moving before you can steer it. Concentrate on moving the leaders.

▶ **TWO HANDLERS**
With two handlers, one person walks in position 2, the other person walks with the leader. The lead handler stays just behind the lead cow's point of balance. Use the same handling pattern, alternating in and out of the flight zone. The two handlers stay close together so that cattle cannot escape between them. The herd instinct for following will pull the tail-enders along.

▶ STRAGGLERS

Don't go behind and chase them! Approach to one side of their head and move just past the point of balance at their shoulder. As soon as the movement of the herd attracts the straggler repeat the alternating herding pattern.

Figure 6. Moving stragglers

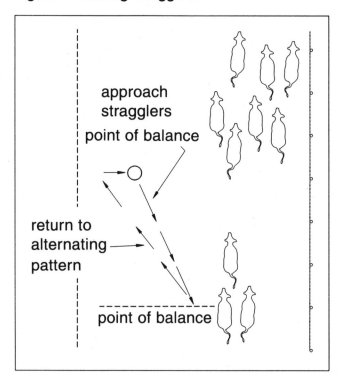

▶ HOW TO FILL A CORRAL

Cattle will be more orderly if they have to walk past you as they enter a corral. Move back and forth straight into the herd to increase and decrease pressure on the flight zone. Apply enough pressure to keep them from veering away from the fence, but not too much to cause panic.

Figure 7. How to fill a corral

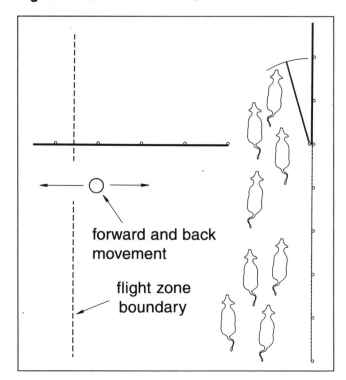

▶ HOW TO EMPTY A CORRAL

Make the animals walk past you. Wait for the animals to turn and look at you before you walk away from the gate.

To empty the pen move back and forth as shown in the diagram.

To sort animals in an alley or by a gate, move forward and backward, not sideways. Increase the pressure on the animals you wish to hold, decrease the pressure on the animals that you wish to let go. Use this pattern to separate cows from calves.

Handle small groups.

Figure 8. How to empty a corral

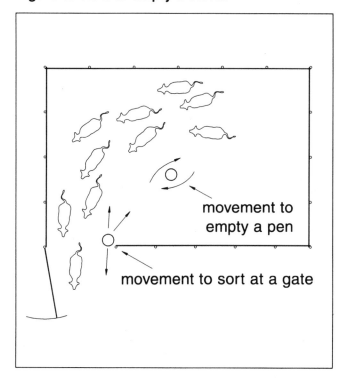

movement to empty a pen

movement to sort at a gate

CORRAL
D·E·S·I·G·N

The purpose of the handling system is to sort, handle and treat cattle.

For any number of cattle, the requirements of a handling system are:

• Collection alley to move cattle fromthe feedlot, pasture or barn to the holding pens. The collection alley can also be used as a holding pen.

• Sorting pens opening off the collection alley. The sorting pen can also be located after the working area.

Figure 9. Handling system requirements

• Holding pens to hold either the whole herd in small operations or groups of 30 to 50 cattle for larger operations.

• Crowding pen or tub to move small groups of eight to 10 cattle into the working area.

• Single file working chute at least 20 feet long to hold three or four cattle at once.

• Loading chute.

• Squeeze or headgate.

• Options such as scales, dark box for artificial insemination (A.I.), calf squeeze or table ...

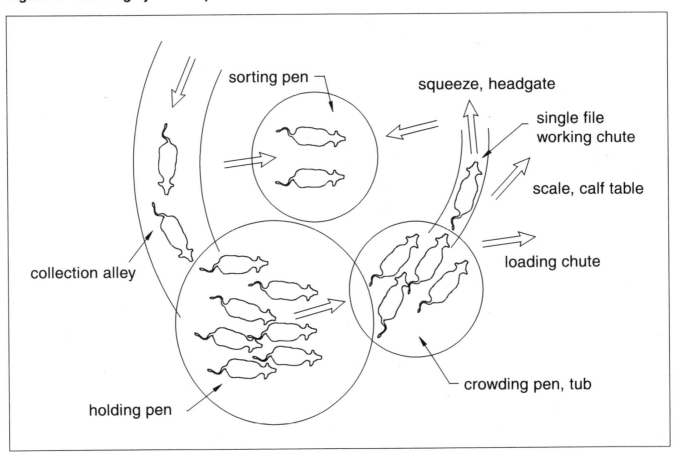

▶ COLLECTION ALLEY

Build the collection alley 10 to 16 feet wide. Too wide an alley allows cattle to circle around the handler. Too narrow means that your tractor won't fit. The collection alley also makes a good long narrow holding pen. Put in gates to divide the cattle into smaller groups.

▶ SORTING PENS

Cattle will easily sort back into angled sorting pens. Putting the pen at an angle helps as it allows cattle to see into the pen before they enter. Move the cattle past the pen, then let them move back into the sorting pen.

Figure 10. Collection alley

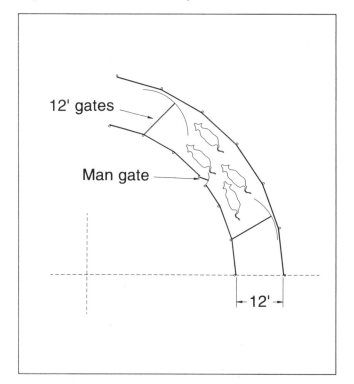

Figure 11. Sorting pens

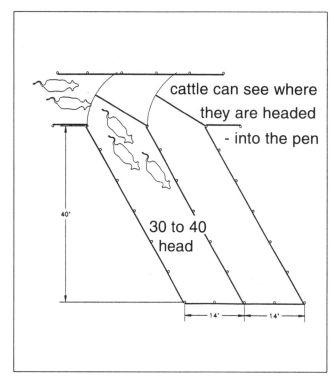

▶ SORTING ALLEY

Another type of sorting gate to divert cattle uses a single file chute. An eight inch high step platform, just ahead of the sorting gate, will make the cattle hesitate for a couple of seconds at the end of the chute - time to allow animal ahead to clear the gate and time for the handler to swing the sorting gate.

When not in use, swing the 12 foot gate back against the collection alley fence. The single file alley can be up to 36 inches wide and quite a bit longer if desired. You can sort into several pens. Operate the sorting gate with a long rope if desired.

Figure 12. Sorting alley

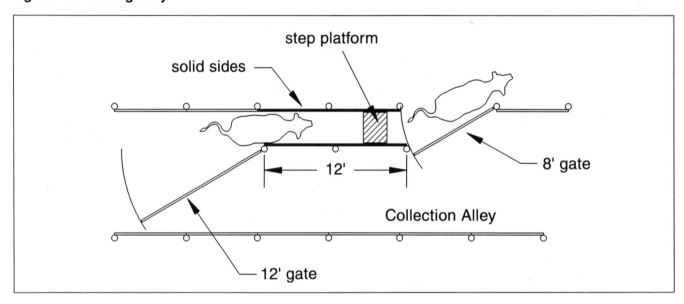

Figure 13. Long sorting alley

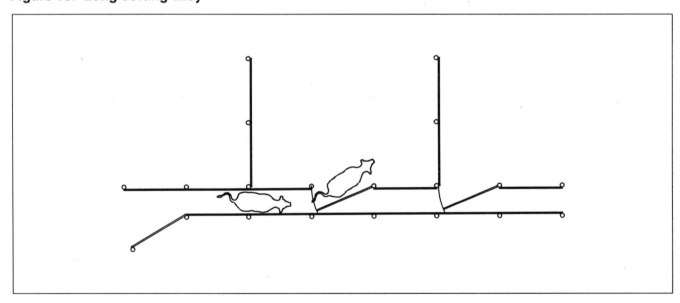

► HOLDING PENS

For small herds, 60 to 80 cattle, make the holding pen large enough to hold the entire herd. For operations of up to 250 cattle put in one holding pen for 40 to 50 animals. For every 250 head, add another holding pen.

It is easier to move cattle through long narrow pens where a gate serves as the end of the pen.

For safety while moving cattle on foot, a 14 inch pass will let you escape from the pen. Safety posts, three to four feet from fence corners, are another option.

Figure 14. Holding pens

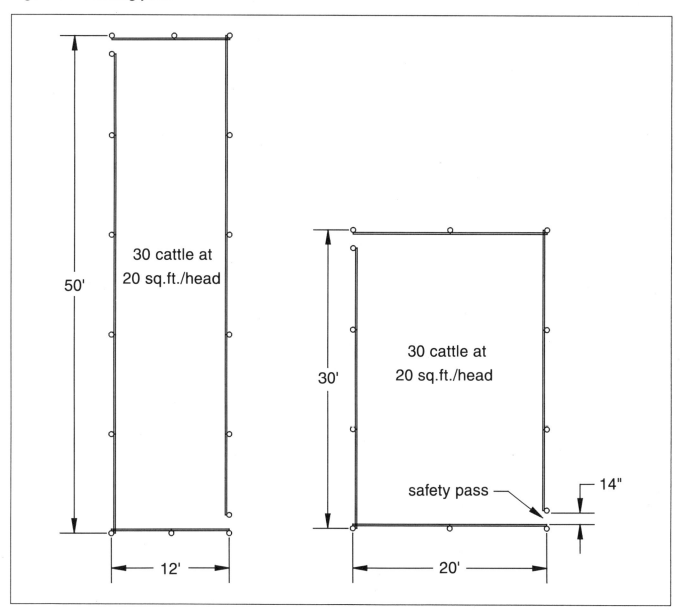

50'

30 cattle at
20 sq.ft./head

12'

30'

30 cattle at
20 sq.ft./head

safety pass

14"

20'

► HOLDING PEN AREA

	Under 600 lb.	600-1200 lb.	over 1200 lb.
Worked immediately-square feet (sq.ft) per animal	14 sq.ft.	17 sq.ft.	20 sq.ft.
Held overnight (sq.ft.) per animal	45 sq.ft.	50 sq.ft.	60 sq.ft
	under 300 kg	300-500 kg	Over 500 kg (cow/calf operations

► COW CALF HOLDING PEN AREA

Animals	30	40	50	60
Worked immediately	600 sq.ft.	800 sq.ft.	1000 sq.ft.	1200 sq.ft
Based on 20 square per animal	12'x50'	12'x70'	12'x85'	12'x100'
	20'x30'	20'x40'	20'x50'	20'x60'

► CIRCULAR CROWDING PEN AREA

Gate radius	8 ft.	10 ft.	12 ft.	14 ft.
1/4 circle	50 sq.ft.	75 sq.ft.	110 sq.ft.	150 sq.ft.
1/2 circle	100 sq.ft.	150 sq.ft.	220 sq.ft.	300 sq.ft

▶ CROWDING PENS

To move cattle from a large holding pen to a single file working chute, use a small crowding pen or crowding tub that handles eight to 10 cattle at a time. Give the animals some room to turn. Follow the animals with a gate as they follow the leader into the single file working chute. The crowding pen is really a small variable sized pen!

WARNING: Don't leave an animal alone in a crowding pen after the others have entered the working chute. A major source of handler injury is an agitated cow charging the handler while trying to rejoin its penmates.

Features of Crowding Pen Design
• **Solid sides and solid crowd gate.**

The solid walls act like blinders on a horse, the cattle can't see distractions outside the pen. They will leave by the one open path being the entrance to the single file working chute.

• **Catwalk**

A raised walkway 18 inches wide around the crowding pen allows the handler to see over the fence and follow the cattle. The height of the catwalk is 36 to 42 inches below the top of the crowding pen fence (the fence will be a belt buckle height when you stand on the catwalk). Remember to put a stair step somewhere as its a long step up to the catwalk.

• **Optional escape board**

Nail a 2 x 6 or 2 x 4 at a 24 inch height along the solid side inside the crowding tub. It makes a toe ledge if you have to make a quick exit from the pen. Bevel the ends to prevent cattle injuries.

• **Man escape gates**

Install man gates at strategic locations for escape purposes or for easy access to pens. Specifications = 18 inches wide, spring loaded, no latches, open inward toward cattle.

Funnel Crowd Pen

The simplest design is to build the pen with one straight side and the other at a 30° angle to prevent cattle from jamming.

Figure 15. Funnel crowd pen

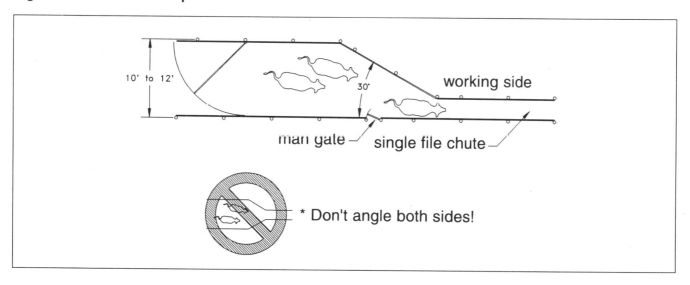

▶ CIRCULAR CROWDING PENS

These are very effective as cattle can see one escape route through the single file working chute. The two layouts show both possible methods of attaching the crowding pen to the working chute.

▶ CROWDING GATE

Use a solid gate to keep cattle from seeing through it. A three to four inch steel pipe in concrete, makes a good pivot post. If the height is adjustable, you can compensate for snow and manure. Several latching points along the crowding pen wall are useful.

Figure 16. Crowding pen with inside catwalk

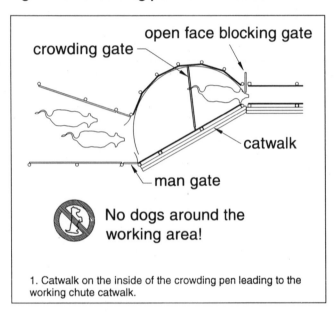

1. Catwalk on the inside of the crowding pen leading to the working chute catwalk.

Figure 18. Crowding gate

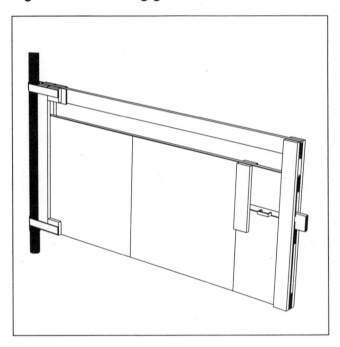

Figure 17. Crowding pen with outside catwalk

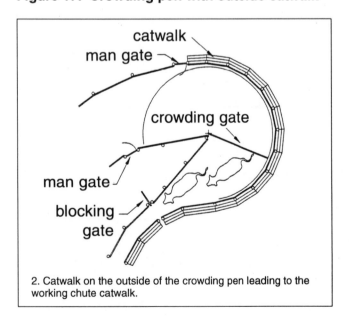

2. Catwalk on the outside of the crowding pen leading to the working chute catwalk.

▶ 360° CROWDING PEN

This design is popularized in layouts from New Zealand. One crowding gate is locked in place. The second gate follows the cattle into the working chute. When the second gate has revolved 360° it is latched and the first gate follows the next batch of cattle. The gates are always moving in the same direction. The crowding gate in this pen can be an open see-through design. The second group of cattle can watch and follow the first group.

Figure 19. 360 degree crowding pen

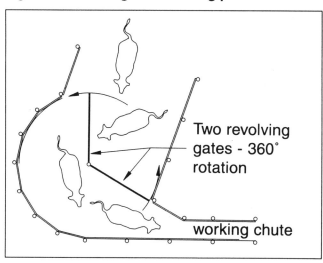

Two revolving gates - 360° rotation

working chute

▶ WORKING CHUTE

The purpose of a single file chute is to hold cattle in a line so they can enter the treatment or loading area one at a time.

Curved chutes work best for animals waiting for treatment. Circular chutes and crowding pens can reduce handling time by up to 50%. (Proceedings of the Australian Society of Animal Production, 1982). For cattle running freely through the chute (not stopped for handling) it makes no difference, curved or straight.

Advantages of curved working chutes are:
• Takes advantage of the cattle's natural circling behavior.
• A solid sided chute doesn't let the cattle see the truck, people, or squeeze until they are almost through it.

Length of Working Chute
-20 feet (minimum) to 50 feet. If cattle can see two body lengths ahead, it doesn't look like they are walking into a dead end. Maximum curve is a 15° angle. This means a 16 foot or greater radius for a curved chute.

Figure 20. Typical single file working chute

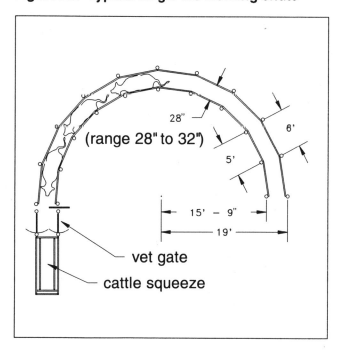

28"
(range 28" to 32")
6'
5'
15' – 9"
19'
vet gate
cattle squeeze

▶ SINGLE FILE CHUTE CAPACITY

Outside radius of chute	Chute length	Number of Cattle
16'	45'	8 cows
20'	60'	10 cows
24'	70'	12 cows

Width - Look at your cattle!

The widest animal in your herd shouldn't get stuck in the chute.

Twenty-eight to 32 inches of width will suit most cattle. For uniform sized animals, straight sides are okay. For handling calves and smaller animals narrowed chutes are needed. Two options used to vary the chute width are to taper it or use temporary filler panels.

• Calves

A filler panel made from sheets of plywood, framed with 2 x 6s hanging from the top of one fence, will reduce the width by six inches.

• Tapered Chutes

Two designs are shown, a full tapered chute and a half tapered chute.

Fully Tapered. Recommendations for the bottom width are 15-18 inches. Make the bottom narrow enough to fit your calves. The width at 32-36 inches above ground level still has to be 28-32 inches.

Figure 21. Single file working chute design

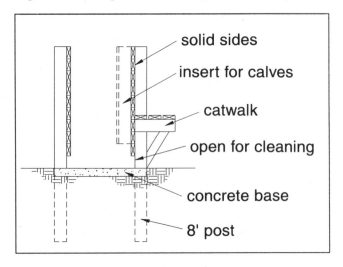

Figure 22. Straight sided chute design

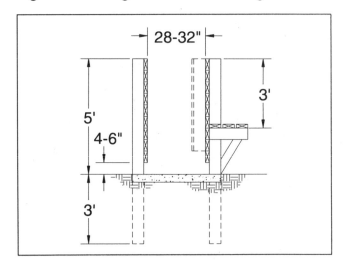

Figure 23. Fully tapered chute

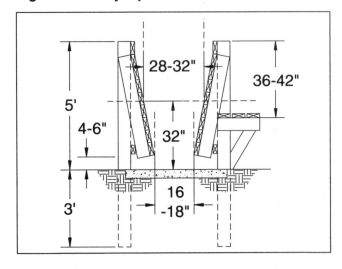

Half Tapered. Build the half slope version 16-18 inches wide at ground level and 28-32 inches wide at 30-32 inches above grade. Above this the walls are straight.

Tapered chutes may be a problem with cattle that go down or topple backwards. If an animal rears up in a chute, back out of its flight zone. Some chutes have overhead bars to keep animals from rearing up and turning around or falling backwards.

Height

The working chute can be five feet or six feet high with solid sides to prevent cattle from seeing outside. The critical height for chute width is at 32-36 inches above ground level. Here the chute needs to be wide enough for the large animals in your herd.

Don't prod or push an animal in a single file chute until it has a place to go. Wait until the tailgate of the squeeze chute is open. Figure 24 is easier to build. After the posts are set, nail a 2 x 4 along the inside at the bottom. This serves as a form for the concrete as well as a support for the tapered side.

Figure 24. Half tapered chute

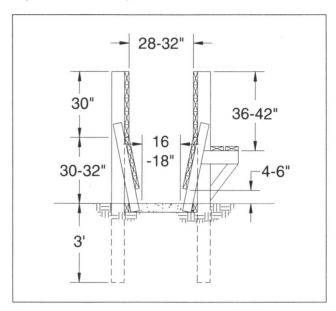

▶ MINIMUM WORKING CHUTE WIDTH

	Under 600 lb.	600-1200 lb.	over 1200 lb.
Straight sided chute	18"	22"	28"
Fully tapered chute -width at 32 in. height	18"	22"	28"
Fully tapered chute -width at bottom	15"	16"	18"
	under 270 kg	270-540 kg	over 540 kg (cow-calf operations)

► CATWALK

A catwalk with a minimum width 18 inches, or wide enough to provide a comfortable surface, allows the handler to see over the solid chute sides and follow the cattle.

Locate the catwalk on the inside curve of the chute. This allows the handler to stand at a 45° to 60° angle behind the animal's shoulder.

The catwalk height should be 36 to 42 inches below the top of the working chute fence or at belt buckle height. With any less, there is a danger of toppling into the chute. Build a step as the catwalk will be quite a height above ground level.

Figure 25. Catwalk location

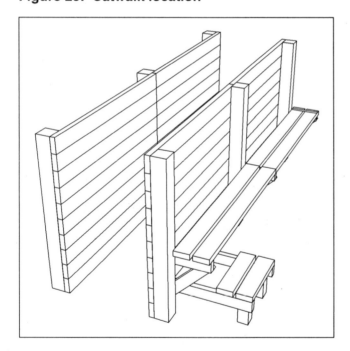

► SOLID SIDES

The sides are solid to prevent animals seeing distractions outside the chute. A six inch gap from ground level to the lowest board on the chute will allow for manure cleanout. It also eliminates wet insect breeding areas.

A 2 x 4 or 2 x 6 escape board, 24 inches above ground inside the wall of a straight working chute, is a good safety feature.

Option - a four inch gap in the solid fence, at cow belly height, will allow a handler at ground level to see an animal's location as it moves along the chute.

A nail width gap between 2 x 6s forming the solid wall will allow water to drain from between the planks. This prevents rotting wood. Use washers on the nails, this prevents the heads from pulling through the wood when cattle push against the opposite side of the fence. It also makes it easier to remove planks.

► GATES

Blocking gates at the entrance and exit of the working chute prevent unwanted animal movement. The gate at the entrance or between the crowding tub and chute should be open or "see through" so that cattle can see an escape path. This prevents balking.

At the exit or between the chute and squeeze the palpation or vet gates should be solid. This prevents cattle seeing a person standing in the chute. Make sure that the blocking gate slides away from the catwalk. You don't want to block the handler's path.

Figure 26. Blocking gate

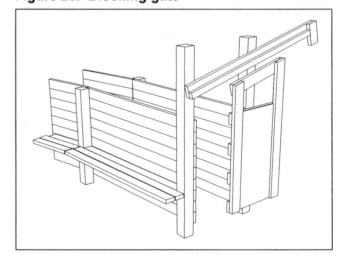

One-way gates or chains allow cattle to move forward in the chute but prevent them from backing up. Locate the gate 12 feet ahead of the squeeze.

The pivoting overhead gate works for cows or calves. Headroom could be a problem for large cattle. A counter weight will make the gate work more smoothly.

For uniform sized cattle a chain makes a good blocking gate. Cows and calves can be handled by varying the chain height. Keep an eight to 12 inch sag in the chain.

Figure 27. One-way gate

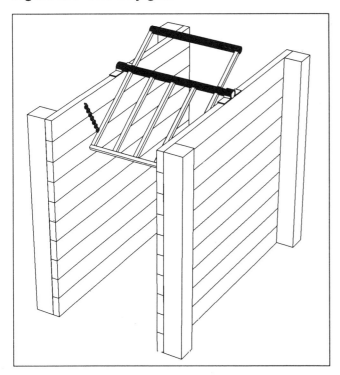

Figure 28. One-way gate - side view

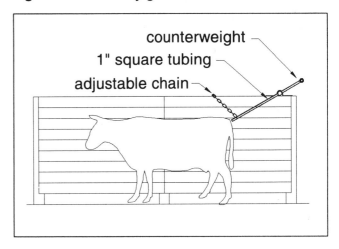

Figure 29. One-way chain gate

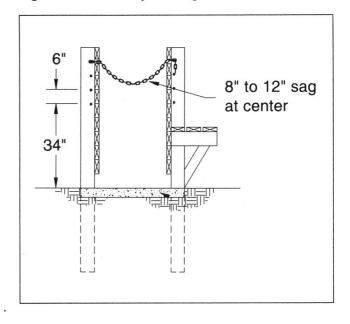

► **CONCRETE FLOOR**

If working chutes are used frequently, a concrete floor is desirable. Be sure to put a deeply grooved pattern in the floor to prevent animals from slipping.

▶ CUTTING GATE OPTION

A cutting gate at the beginning of the chute or ahead of the squeeze can divert cattle not needing treatment.

Figure 30. Cutting gate

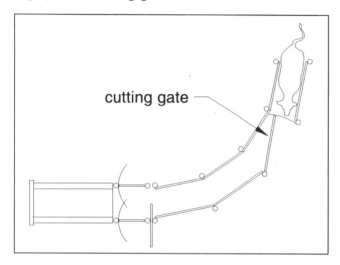

cutting gate

▶ LOADING CHUTE

• Location

Access to an all weather road is important.

Cattle move better directly from the crowding pen to the loading chute, rather than moving through a long working chute.

• Curved shape and solid sides

A curved approach, 30 to 35 inches wide, prevents animals from seeing the truck until they are nearly loaded.

• A height adjustment

of 26 to 45 inches may be required to match various sized trucks. A five foot level landing is desirable for walking on or off the truck.

• Gradual slope

A fixed ramp should have a maximum 20° slope and an adjustable ramp no more than 25°

• Bumpers and side gates

Self-aligning bumpers prevent any gaps between the truck and chute that could injure cattle. Adjustable wing gates close any gaps between loading chute sides and the truck.

• Catwalks

improve access for the handler.

• Steps

are preferred over ramps, along with concrete construction (rough surface). When ramps are used, space 1 x 2 inch hardwood cleats eight inches apart, measured edge to edge.

• An earth ramp

is a good option.

Figure 31. Loading chute geometry

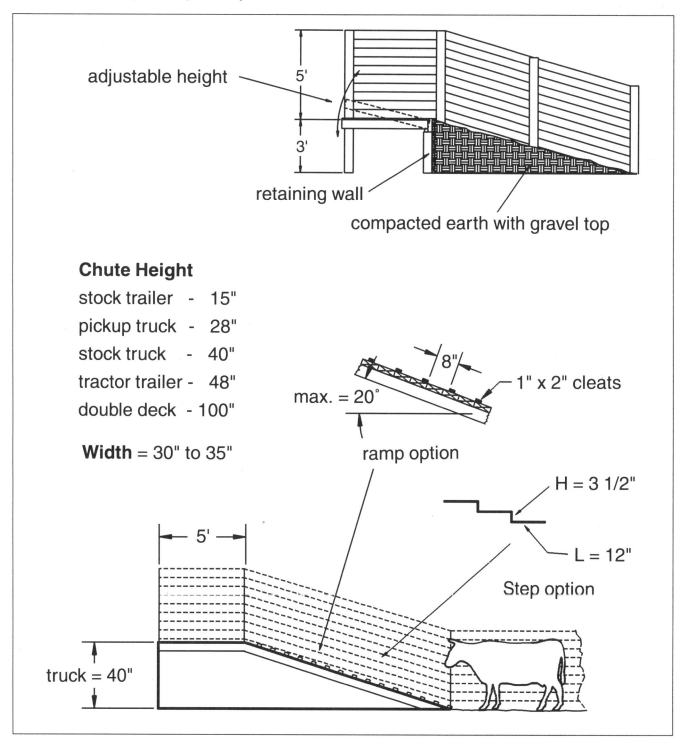

adjustable height

5'

3'

retaining wall

compacted earth with gravel top

Chute Height

stock trailer	-	15"
pickup truck	-	28"
stock truck	-	40"
tractor trailer	-	48"
double deck	-	100"

Width = 30" to 35"

8"

max. = 20°

1" x 2" cleats

ramp option

H = 3 1/2"

L = 12"

Step option

5'

truck = 40"

► LOADING CHUTE LOCATION

Cattle load best if they can go directly from a crowding pen, rather than through a single file chute.

Figure 32. Loading chute location

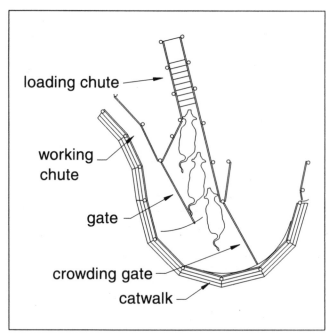

► TRAILER LOADING AREAS

Low bed stock trailers, with 12 inches or less clearance from the ground, need only a drive alley and gates to direct cattle before they step into the trailer.

Figure 33. Trailer loading - option one

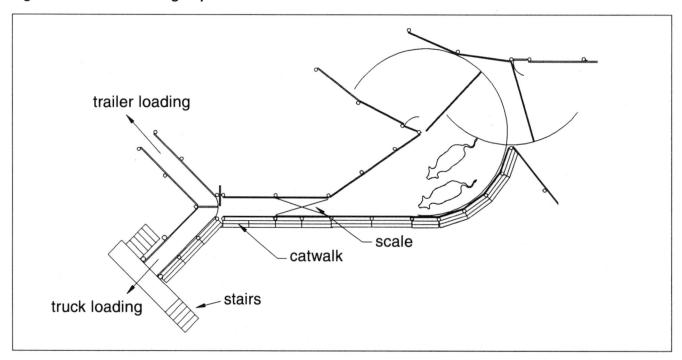

Figure 34. Trailer loading - option two

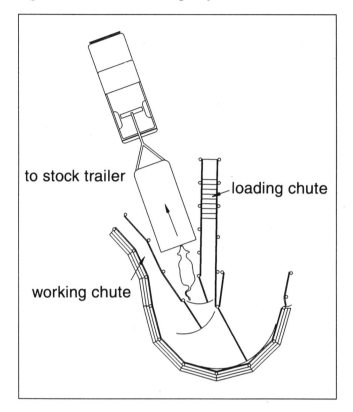

to stock trailer

loading chute

working chute

Figure 35. Trailer loading - option three

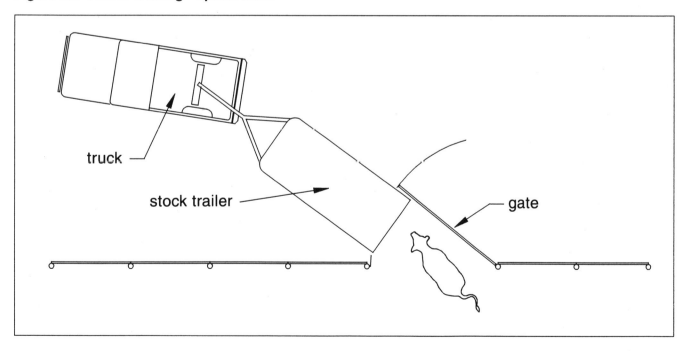

truck

stock trailer

gate

Figure 36. Trailer loading - option four

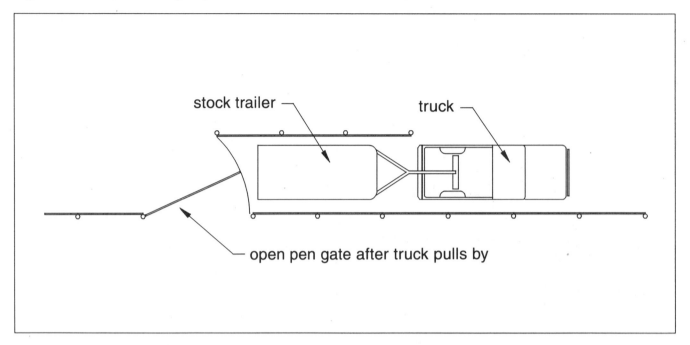

stock trailer

truck

open pen gate after truck pulls by

Figure 37. Trailer loading - option five

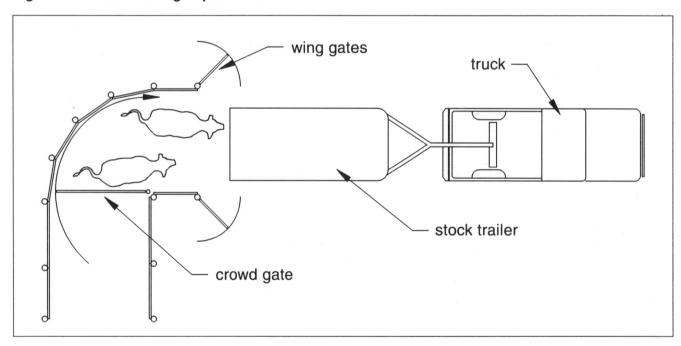

wing gates

truck

stock trailer

crowd gate

▶ WORKING AREA COMBINATIONS

All handling systems consist of a series of individual components. After the crowding, treatment and loading areas have been designed, they must be combined into a working unit that meets the requirements of the operation. Good working areas allow for a smooth flow of cattle and provide convenient access to the cattle for handlers. The proper combination of components in a working area can be the most important factor in the successful operation of handling corrals.

The first consideration in developing a working area is the limitations imposed by the site. The design must be suitable for the amount of space, the topography of the land, co-ordination with other buildings and facilities and vehicle access. Beyond the site considerations, the layout of the working area is largely governed by personal preference and the way cattle are handled on the particular operation.

Several of the possible working area combinations are shown in Figures 38-41. These diagrams illustrate the main factors in working area design.

The factors are listed below:

- Direction of cattle flow on entering and leaving the facility.

- Crowding pen size, curvature and handler location.

- Working chute length, style (half-circle, quarter circle, "S" -curve, straight), direction of curve, and working side.

- Scale design (single or group, combination cattle and truck) and location (inside or adjacent to the working area).

- Loading chute and trailer loading designs and locations; unloading system.

Figure 38. Working area combination - option one

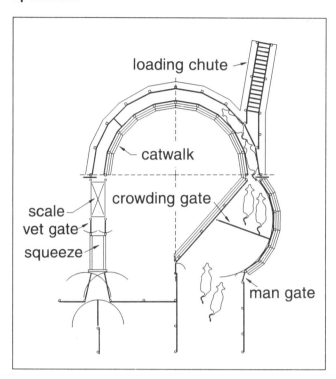

Figure 39. Working area combination - option two

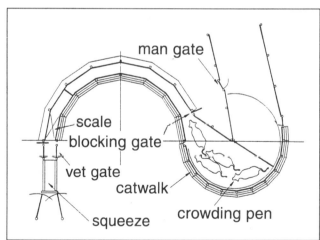

**Figure 40. Working area combination
-option three**

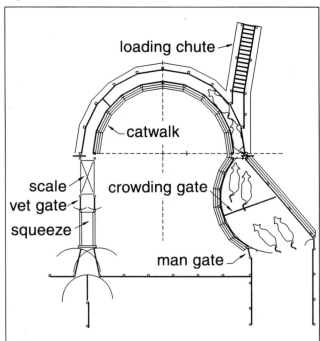

loading chute

catwalk

scale
vet gate
squeeze

crowding gate

man gate

**Figure 41. Working area combination
- option four**

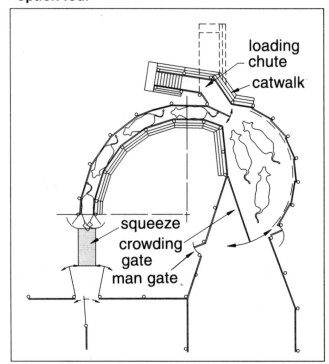

loading
chute

catwalk

squeeze
crowding
gate
man gate

C O R R A L
L·A·Y·O·U·T·S

All the layouts are drawn with the mirror image of any corral plan on the facing page. Both drawings have the same set of dimensions. Reference lines used to locate the center of the working chutes and crowding tubs are drawn with dashed lines.

The number of cattle shown on each plan was calculated taking the area of each pen in square feet and dividing by 20 (square feet per cow).

The cost index shown on the layouts is the relative cost of each layout compared to layout 1.

The minimum working corral cost is one, corral two for example costs 1.35 times as much.

Material cost only was used. No squeeze was included.

All the plans are computer generated using six inch diameter posts and two inch thick planks. The plans are available as Autocad files.

The sources of the various layouts are:

Corral Layout 1, 9
- Canada Plan Service CPS 1831 Adapted by Wayne Winchell, regional engineer, Barrhead, Dennis Darby, farm structures engineer, Lethbridge. CPS 1835 Adapted by Robert Borg, regional engineer, Red Deer.

Corral Layout 2, 3, 4, 18
- Reproduced with permission from: Beef Housing and Equipment Handbook, MWPS-6 4th ed, 1987 (c) MidWest Plan Service, Ames, IA 50011-3080.

Corral Layout 5
- United States Department of Agriculture. Plan adapted by Robert Borg, regional engineer, Red Deer.

Corral Layout 6, 16
- Wayne Winchell, regional engineer, Barrhead.

Corral Layout 17, 19
- Temple Grandin plans adapted by Wayne Winchell, regional engineer, Barrhead.

Corral Layout 7, 8, 15
- Saskatchewan Department of Agriculture.

Corral Layout 10
- Western Regional Agricultural Engineering Service (WRAES).

Corral Layout 11
- Trevor Jones, beef specialist, Fairview.

Corral Layout 12, 13, 14
- Trevor Yurchak, district agriculturist, Sedgewick.

Corral Layout 20
- Dennis Darby, farm structures engineer, Lethbridge.

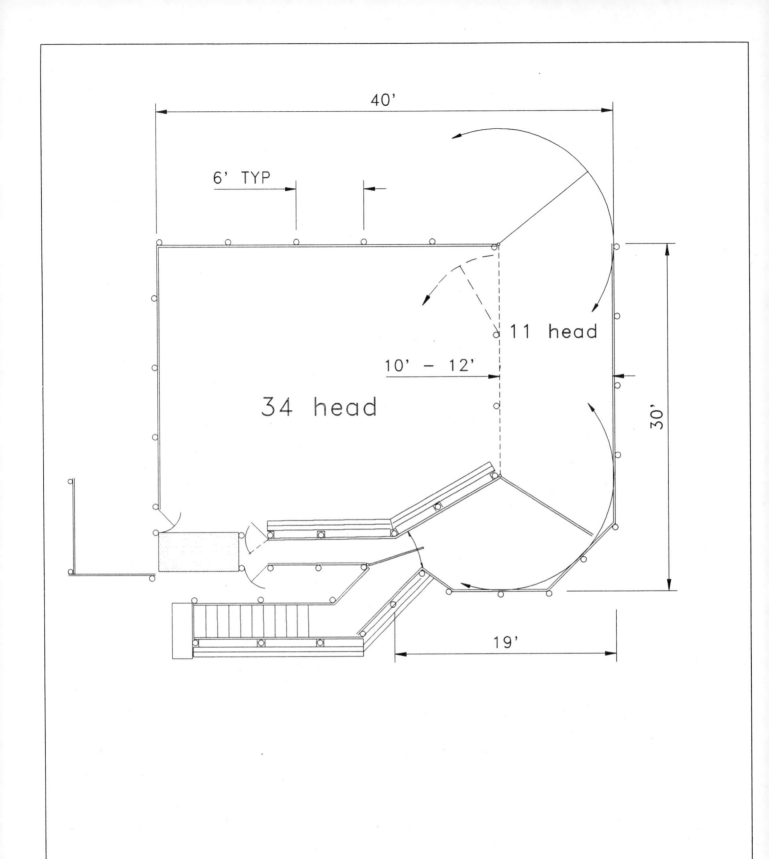

40'

6' TYP

11 head

10' – 12'

34 head

30'

19'

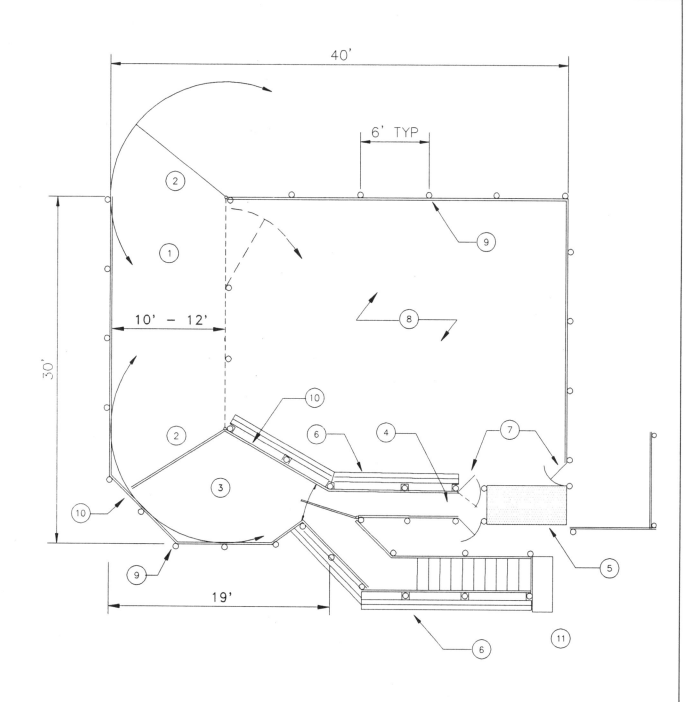

40'

6' TYP

10' – 12'

30'

19'

② crowding gate, 10'–12'

① sorting alley
② crowding gate, 10'–12'
③ crowding tub (solid walls)
④ working chute, inside width 28"–30"

5 squeeze
6 catwalk
7 man gate
8 holding pen

9 6" PT post
10 2 x 6 rough plank
11 loading chute, offset sight line from ③

Material cost, $1200-$1400   **Cost Index - 1.0**

MINIMUM WORKING CORRAL

CORRAL LAYOUT 1

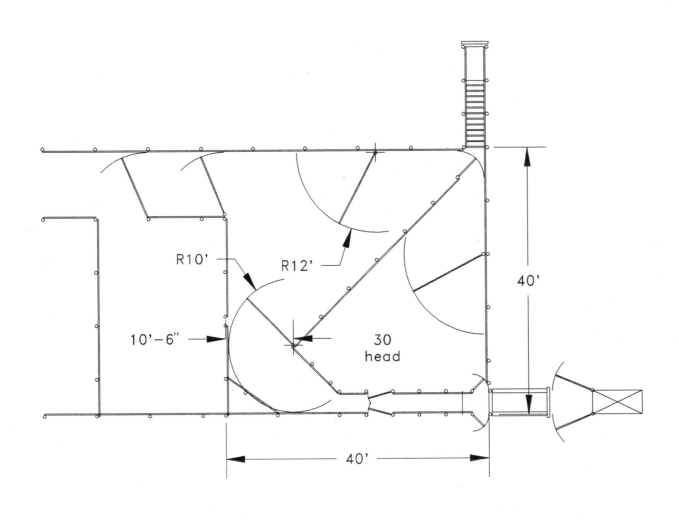

R10'

R12'

10'–6"

30
head

40'

40'

MINIMUM CORRAL TWO **CORRAL LAYOUT 2**

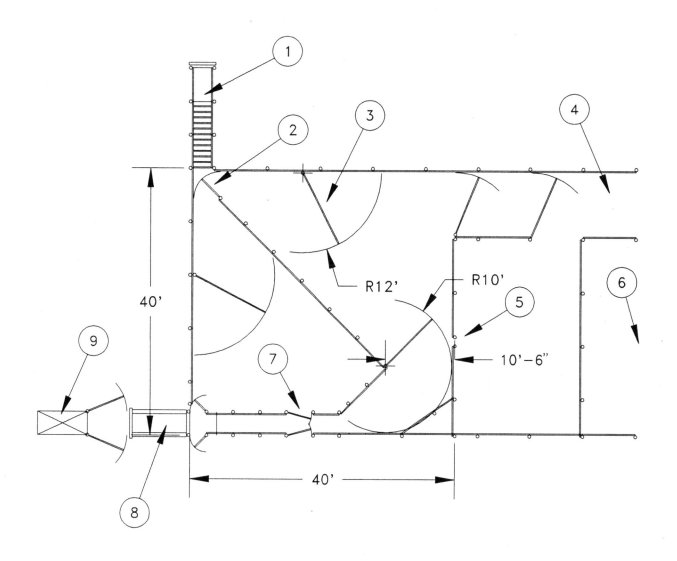

40'

R12'

R10'

10'-6"

40'

1. Loading chute
2. 4' gate
3. 12' crowding gate
4. sorting alley
5. 14" man safety pass

6. Extra holding pens
7. 4' cutting gates
8. Headgate and squeeze
9. Portable scale

Cost Index - 1.35

MINIMUM CORRAL TWO

CORRAL LAYOUT 2

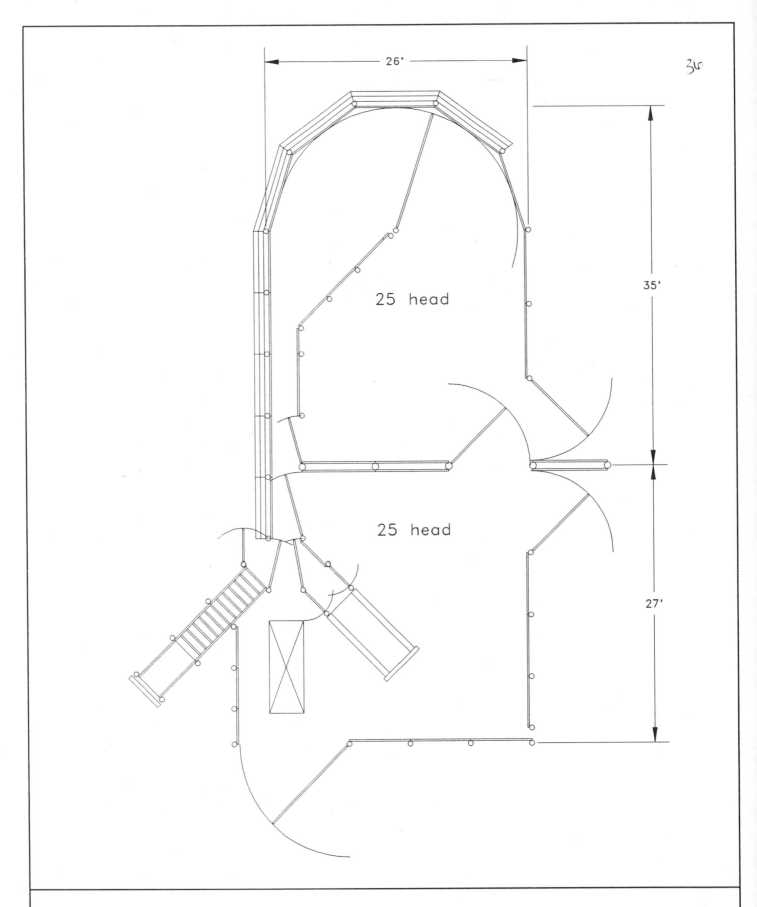

26'

35'

25 head

27'

25 head

MWPS

CORRAL LAYOUT 3

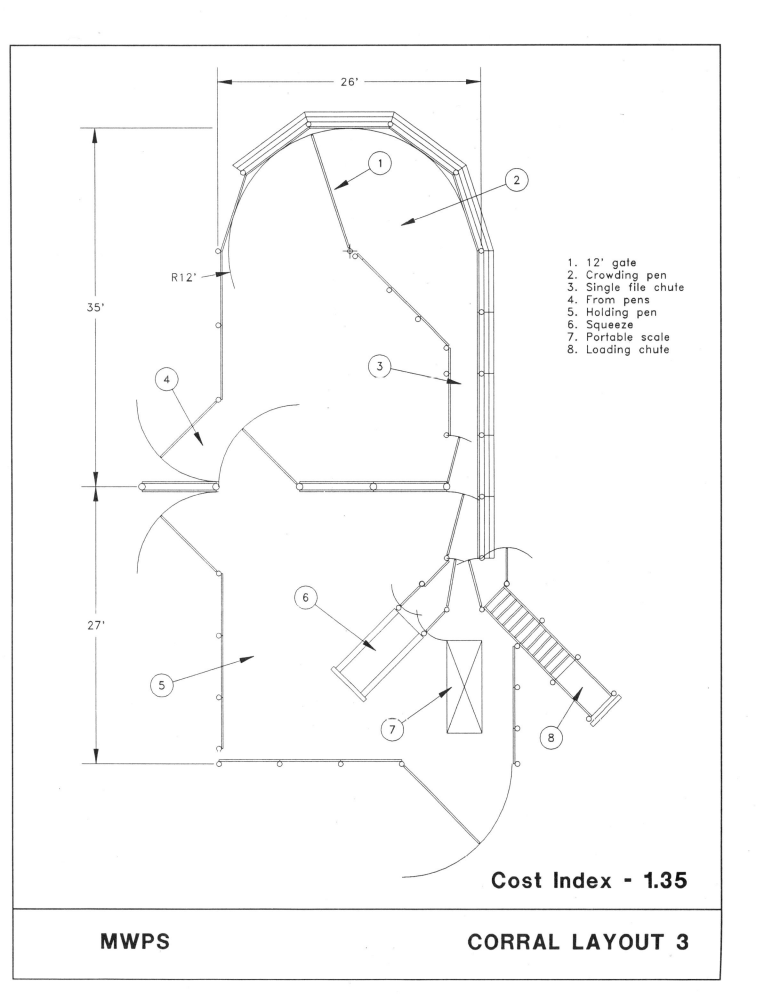

26'

35'

R12'

27'

1. 12' gate
2. Crowding pen
3. Single file chute
4. From pens
5. Holding pen
6. Squeeze
7. Portable scale
8. Loading chute

1
2
3
4
5
6
7
8

Cost Index - 1.35

MWPS

CORRAL LAYOUT 3

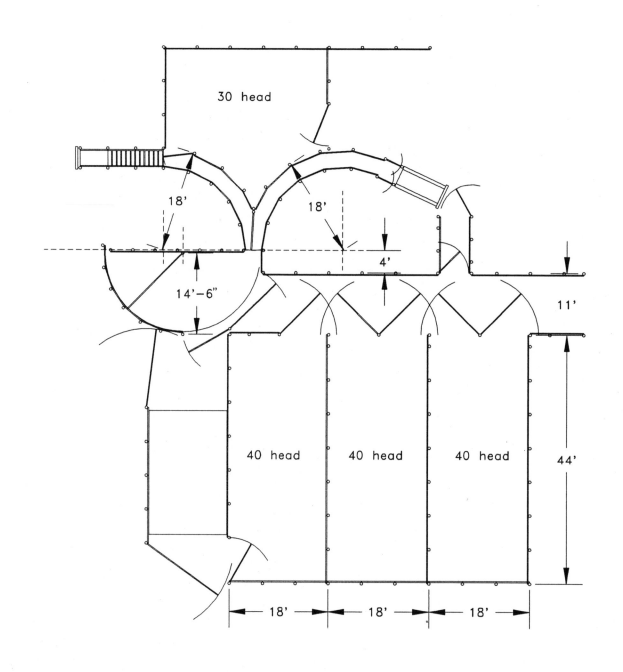

30 head

18'

18'

4'

14'-6"

11'

40 head

40 head

40 head

44'

18'

18'

18'

DOUBLE CIRCLE CORRAL

CORRAL LAYOUT 4

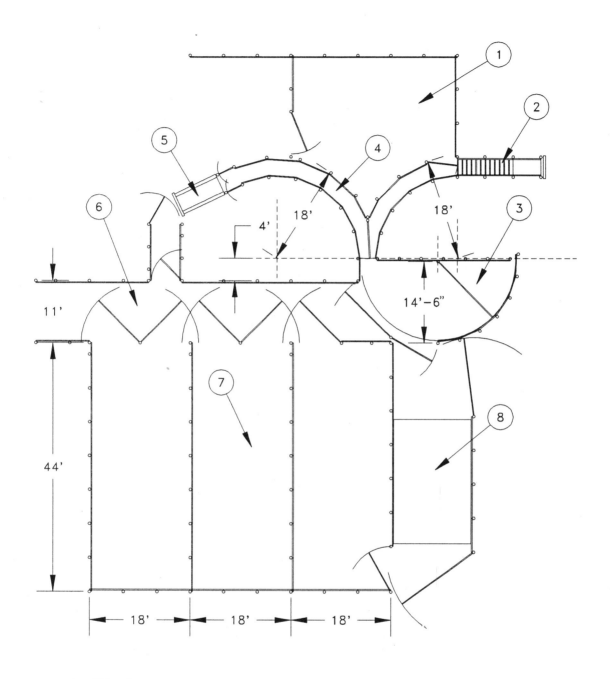

1. Ship in pen
2. Loading chute
3. 14' crowding gate
4. Working chute

5. Squeeze
6. Gathering alley
7. Holding pens
8. 14' x 22' scale

Cost Index - 2.3

DOUBLE CIRCLE CORRAL

CORRAL LAYOUT 4

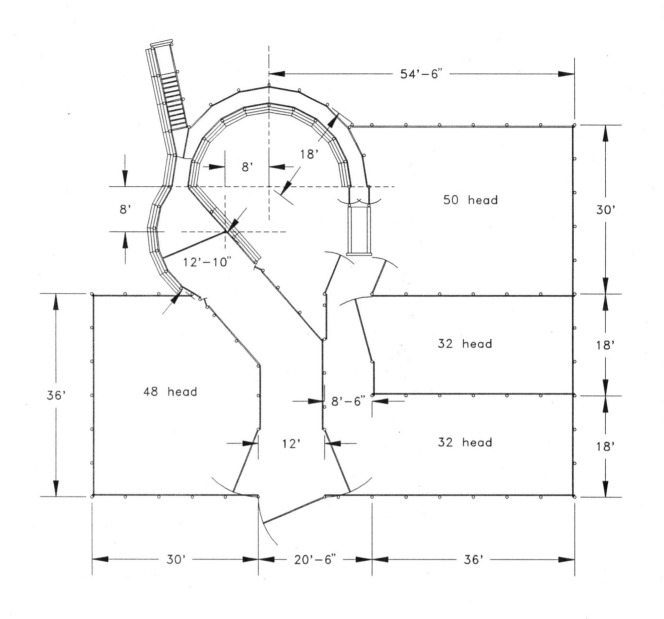

54'–6"

8'

18'

50 head

30'

8'

12'–10"

36'

48 head

32 head

18'

8'–6"

12'

32 head

18'

30'

20'–6"

36'

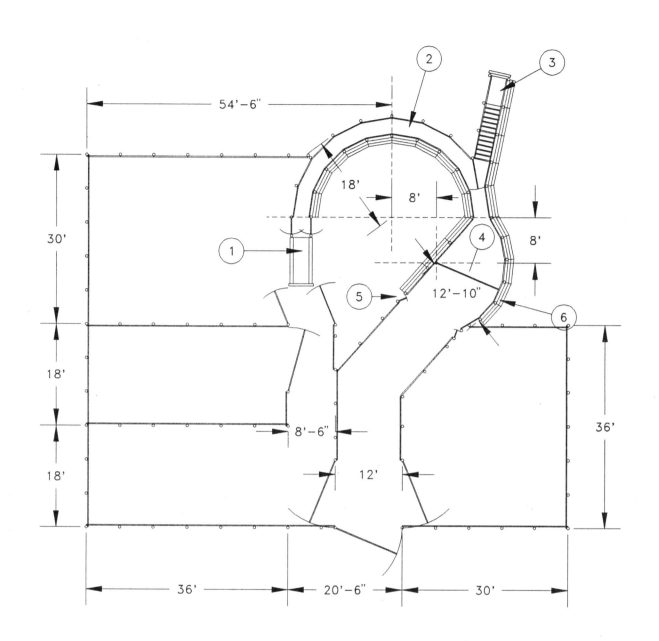

1. Squeeze
2. Working chute
3. Loading chute
4. 12' crowding gate
5. Man gate
6. Catwalk

Cost Index - 2.1

USDA

CORRAL LAYOUT 5

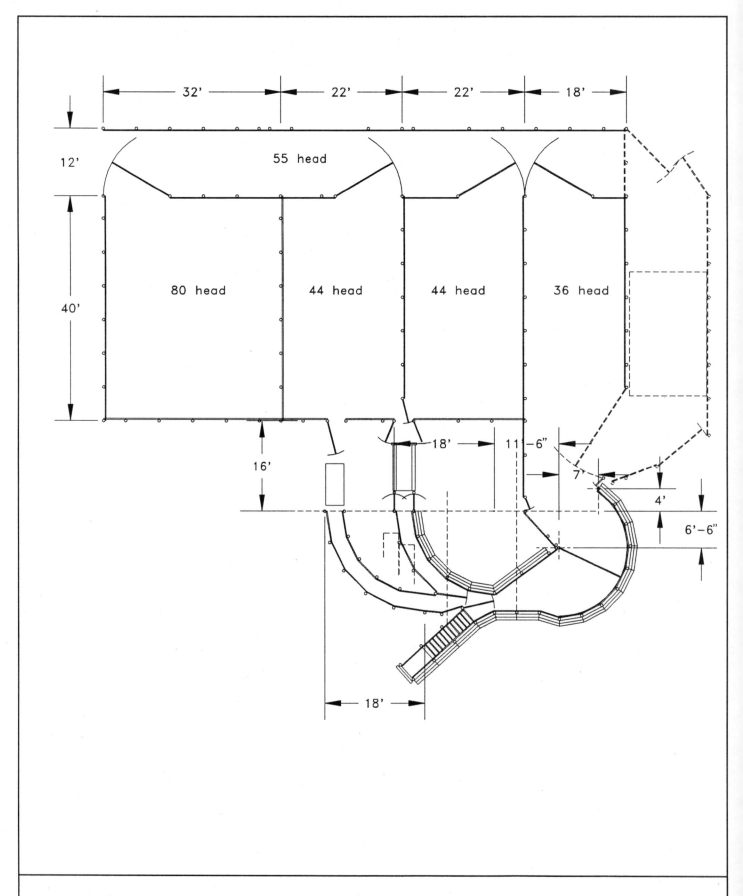

32'　　22'　　22'　　18'

12'

55 head

40'

80 head　44 head　44 head　36 head

16'

18'　11'-6"

7'

4'

6'-6"

18'

WINCHELL PLAN　　　　**CORRAL LAYOUT 6**

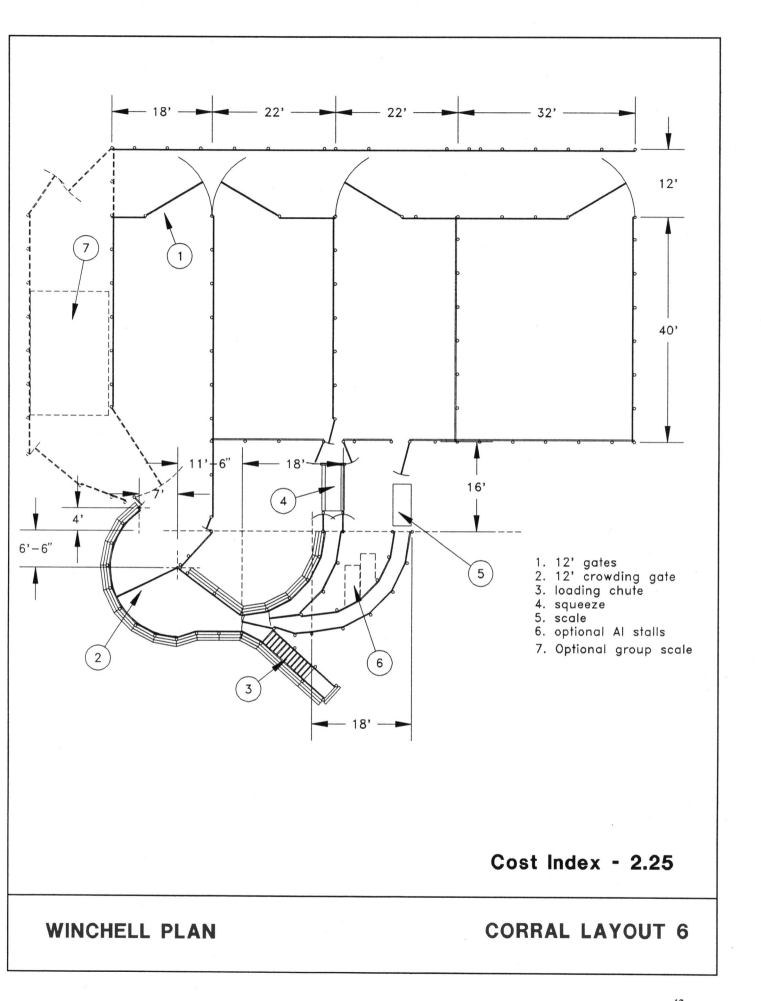

18' 22' 22' 32'

12'

40'

16'

12'

11'-6" 18'

4'

6'-6"

18'

1. 12' gates
2. 12' crowding gate
3. loading chute
4. squeeze
5. scale
6. optional AI stalls
7. Optional group scale

Cost Index - 2.25

WINCHELL PLAN **CORRAL LAYOUT 6**

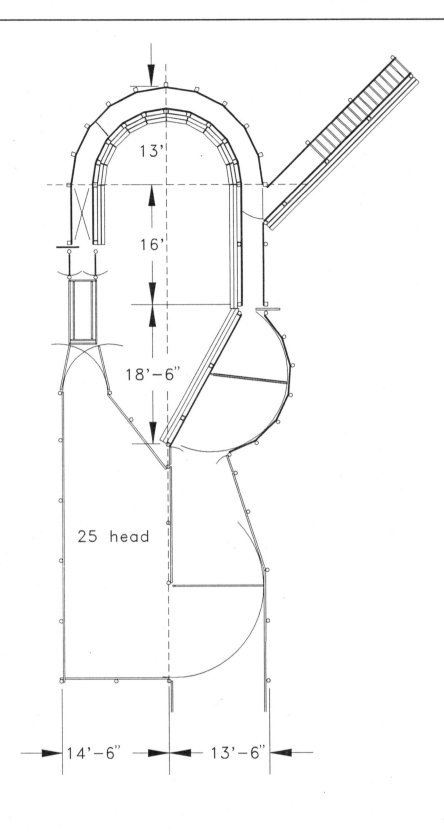

13'

16'

18'—6"

25 head

14'—6"   13'—6"

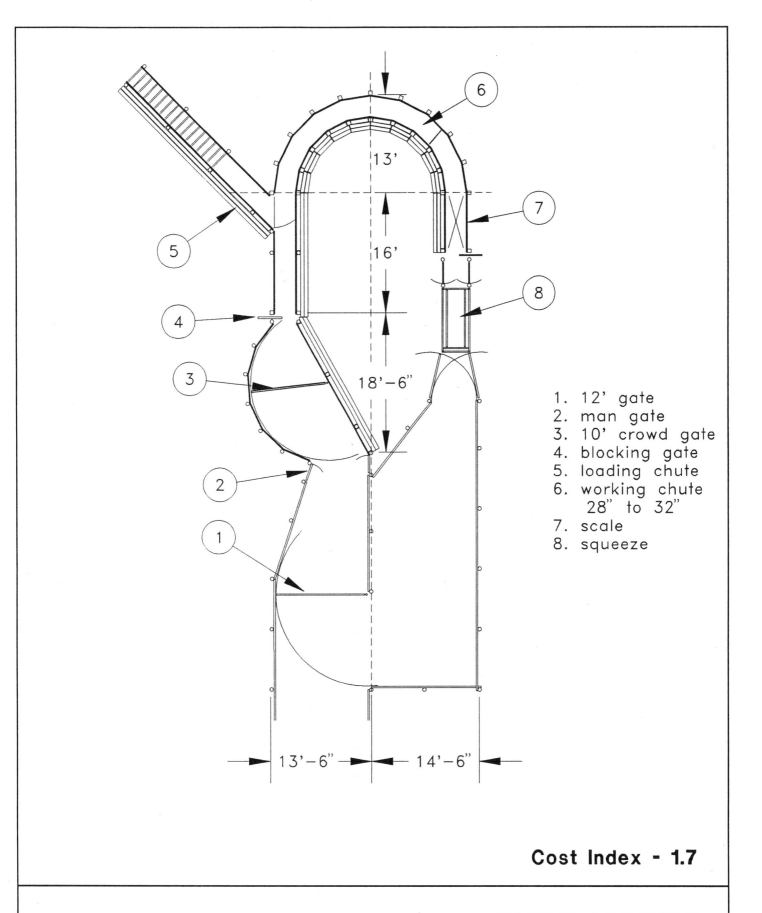

1. 12' gate
2. man gate
3. 10' crowd gate
4. blocking gate
5. loading chute
6. working chute
   28" to 32"
7. scale
8. squeeze

13'

16'

18'-6"

13'-6"   14'-6"

Cost Index - 1.7

SASKATCHEWAN S186

CORRAL LAYOUT 7

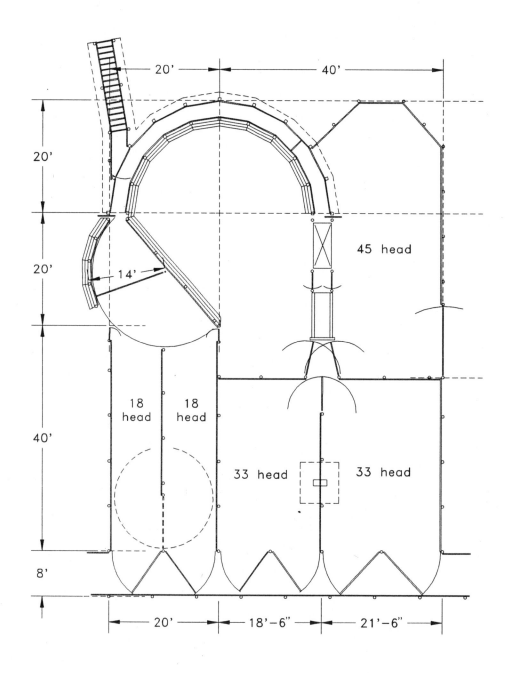

20'   40'

20'

20'

14'   45 head

40'   18 head   18 head

33 head   33 head

8'

20'   18'-6"   21'-6"

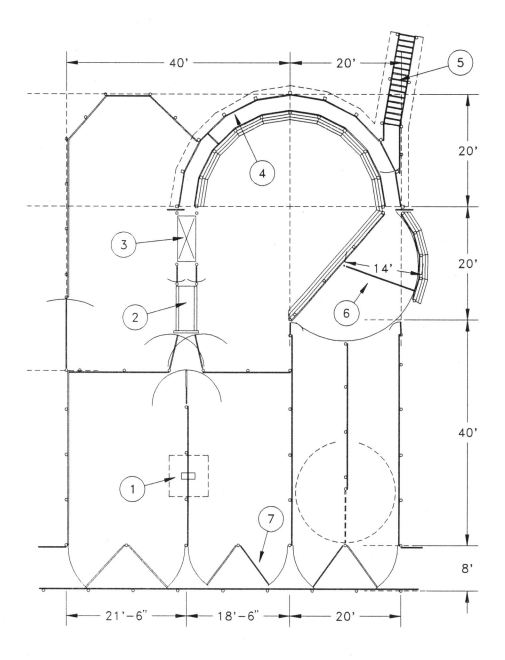

1. Optional waterer for overnight
2. Squeeze
3. Scale
4. Working chute with catwalk
5. Loading chute
6. 14' crowding pen
7. 9' to 10' gates

Cost Index - 2.45

SASKATCHEWAN S185

CORRAL LAYOUT 8

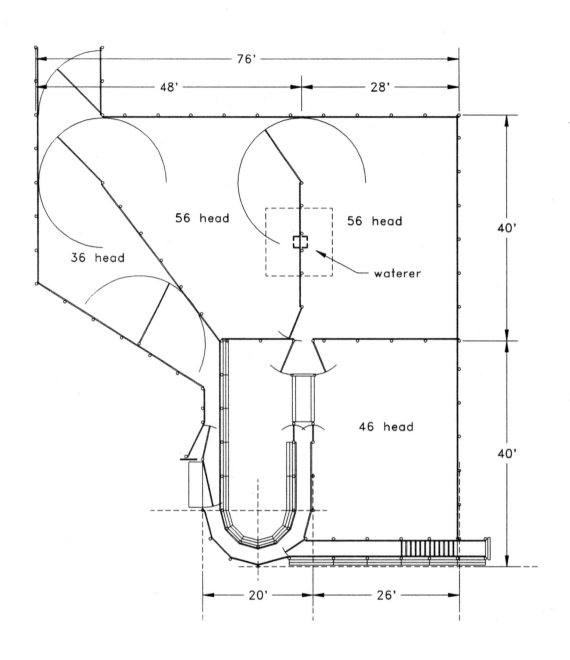

56 head

56 head

36 head

waterer

46 head

76'

48'

28'

40'

40'

20'

26'

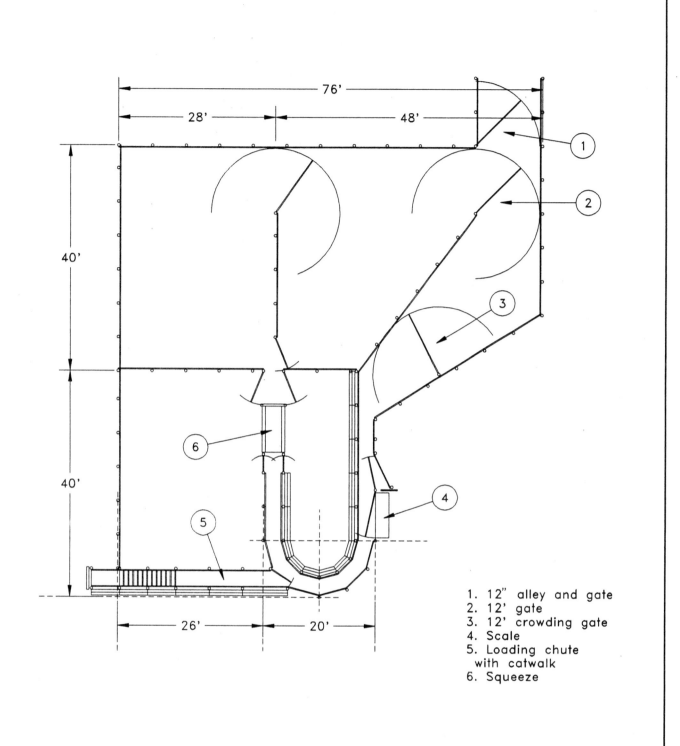

76'

28'

48'

40'

40'

26'

20'

1. 12" alley and gate
2. 12' gate
3. 12' crowding gate
4. Scale
5. Loading chute
   with catwalk
6. Squeeze

Cost Index - 2.1

CPS 1835

CORRAL LAYOUT 9

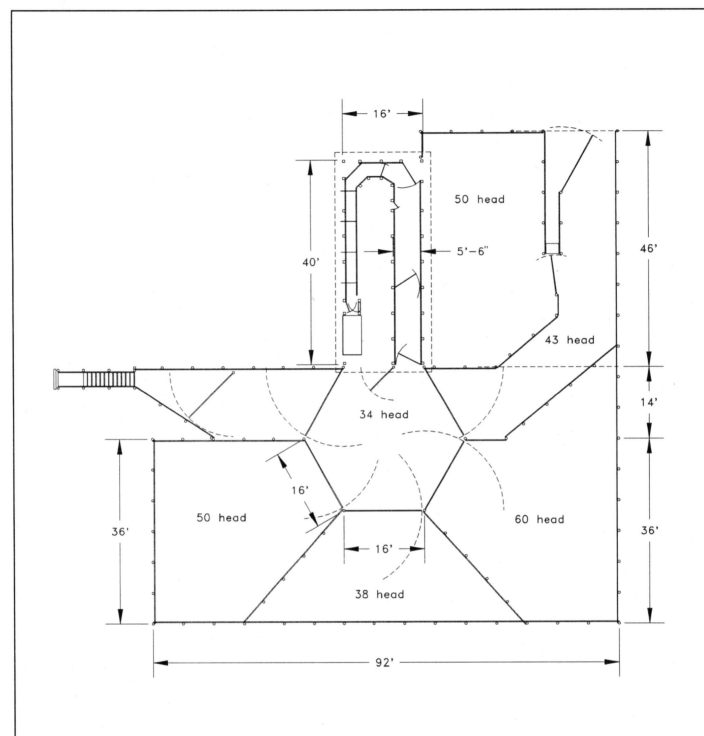

16'

40'

5'–6"

50 head

46'

43 head

34 head

14'

16'

50 head

36'

60 head

36'

16'

38 head

92'

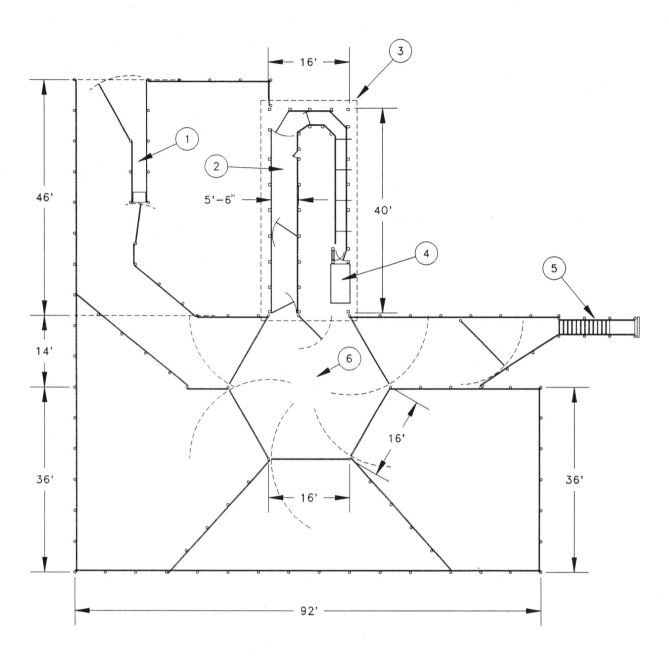

1. Sorting chute
2. Horseshoe corral
3. Optional roofed area
4. Squeeze
5. Loading chute
6. Gathering area

Cost Index - 2.7

WRAES PLAN

CORRAL LAYOUT 10

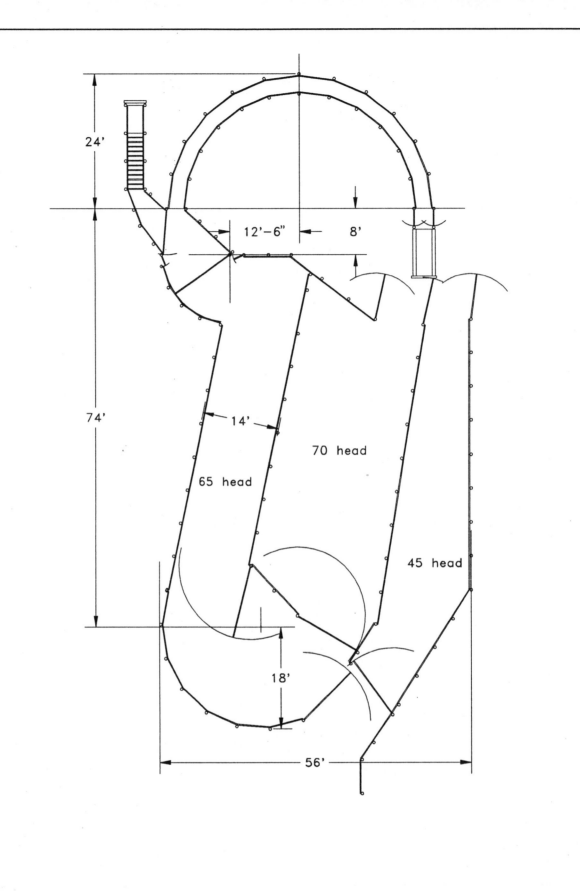

24'

74'

12'-6"   8'

14'

70 head

65 head

45 head

18'

56'

T JONES PLAN

CORRAL LAYOUT 11

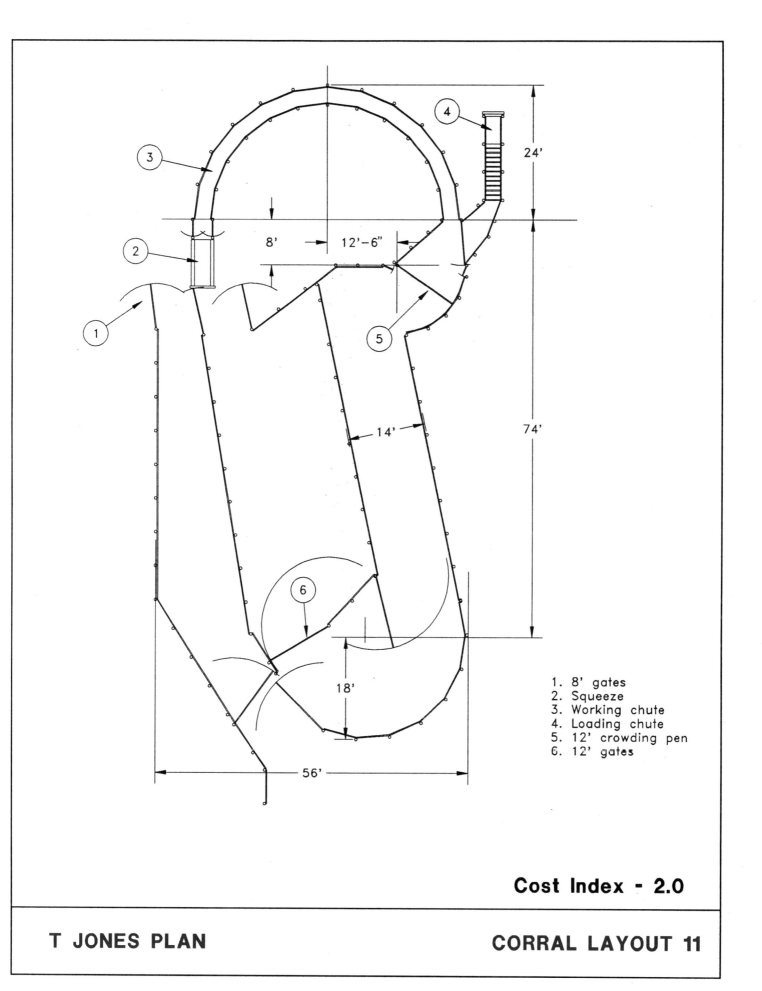

24'

8' → 12'-6"

74'

14'

18'

56'

1. 8' gates
2. Squeeze
3. Working chute
4. Loading chute
5. 12' crowding pen
6. 12' gates

Cost Index - 2.0

T JONES PLAN

CORRAL LAYOUT 11

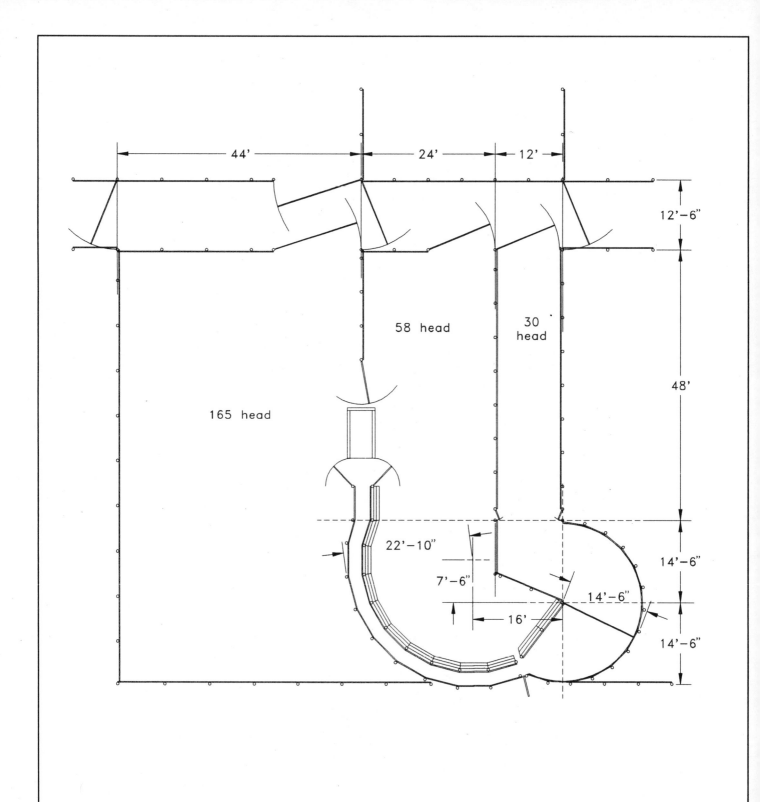

YURCHAK PLAN 1

CORRAL LAYOUT 12

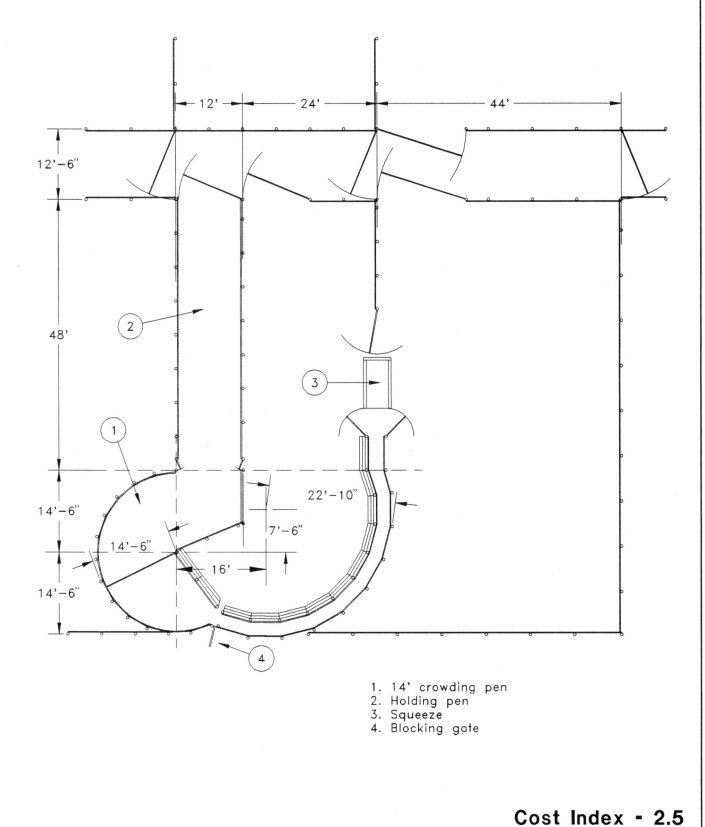

12' 24' 44'

12'-6"

48'

② Holding pen

③ Squeeze

① 14' crowding pen

22'-10"

14'-6"

14'-6"

7'-6"

16'

14'-6"

④

1. 14' crowding pen
2. Holding pen
3. Squeeze
4. Blocking gate

Cost Index - 2.5

YURCHAK PLAN 1

CORRAL LAYOUT 12

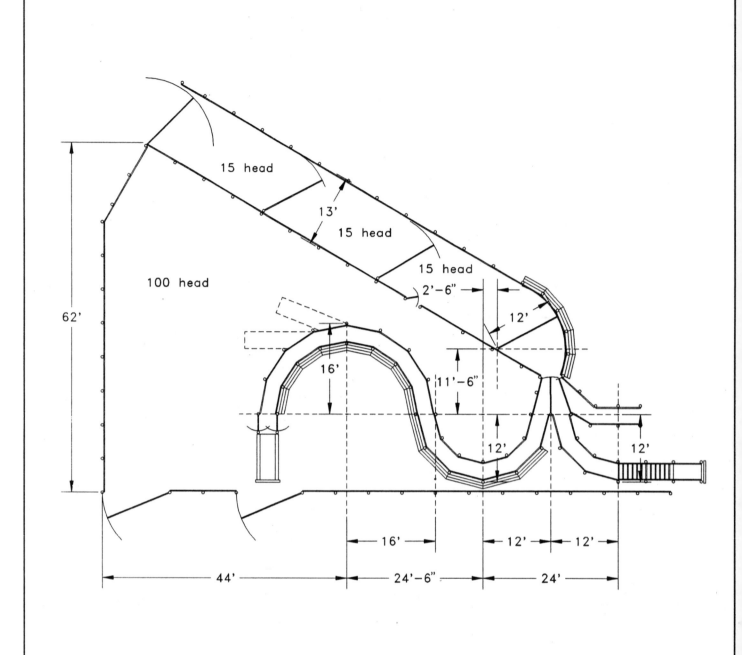

15 head

13'

15 head

100 head

15 head

2'-6"

12'

16'

11'-6"

62'

12'

12'

16'

12'

12'

44'

24'-6"

24'

YURCHAK PLAN 2

CORRAL LAYOUT 13

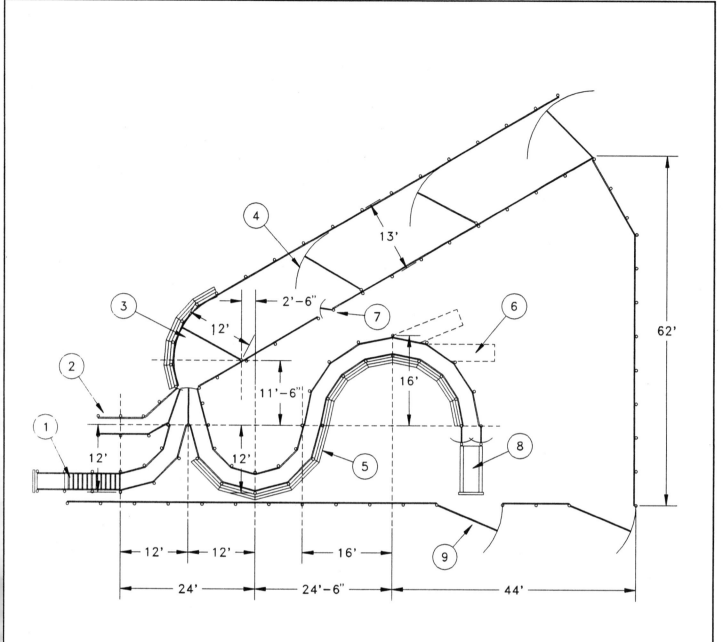

1. Loading chute
2. Trailer loading chute
3. 12' crowding gate
4. Gathering alley
5. Working chute with catwalk (32")
6. AI stalls
7. Man gate
8. Squeeze
9. 10' or 12' gates

Cost Index - 2.25

YURCHAK PLAN 2

CORRAL LAYOUT 13

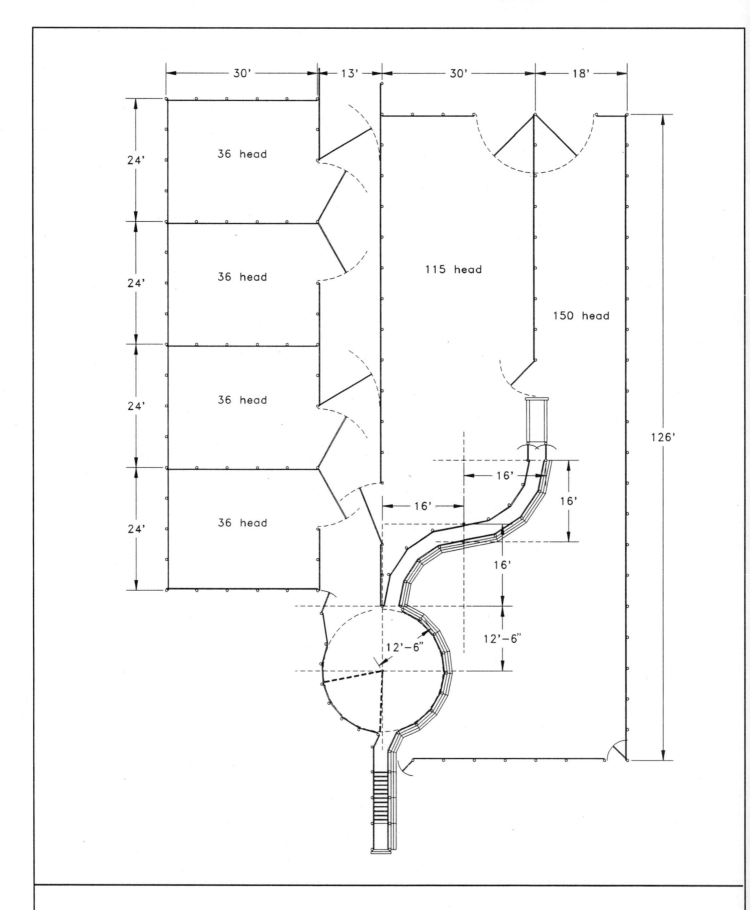

30'   13'   30'   18'

24'

36 head

24'

36 head

115 head

150 head

24'

36 head

24'

36 head

126'

24'

36 head

16'

16'

16'

16'

12'-6"

12'-6"

YURCHAK PLAN 3

CORRAL LAYOUT 14

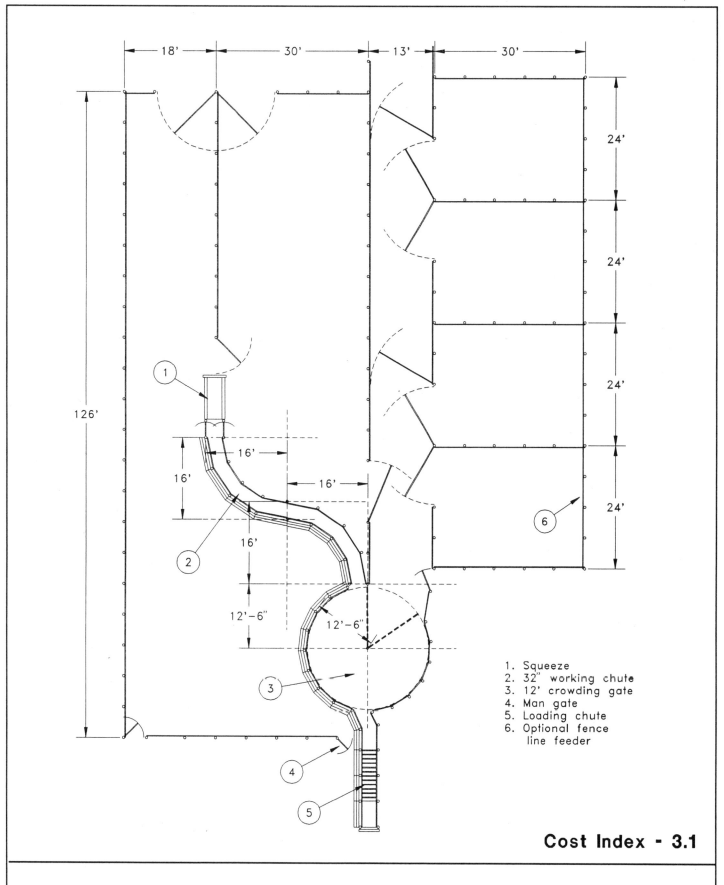

1. Squeeze
2. 32" working chute
3. 12' crowding gate
4. Man gate
5. Loading chute
6. Optional fence
   line feeder

Cost Index - 3.1

YURCHAK PLAN 3

CORRAL LAYOUT 14

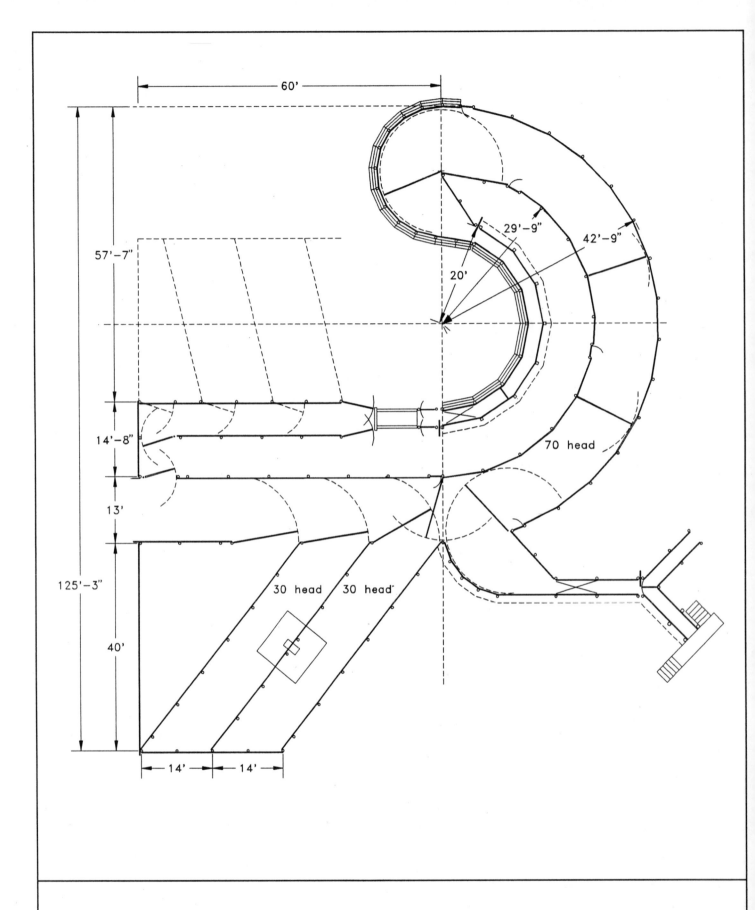

60'

57'—7"

29'—9"

42'—9"

20'

14'—8"

70 head

13'

125'—3"

30 head   30 head

40'

14'   14'

SASKATCHEWAN S187   **CORRAL LAYOUT 15**

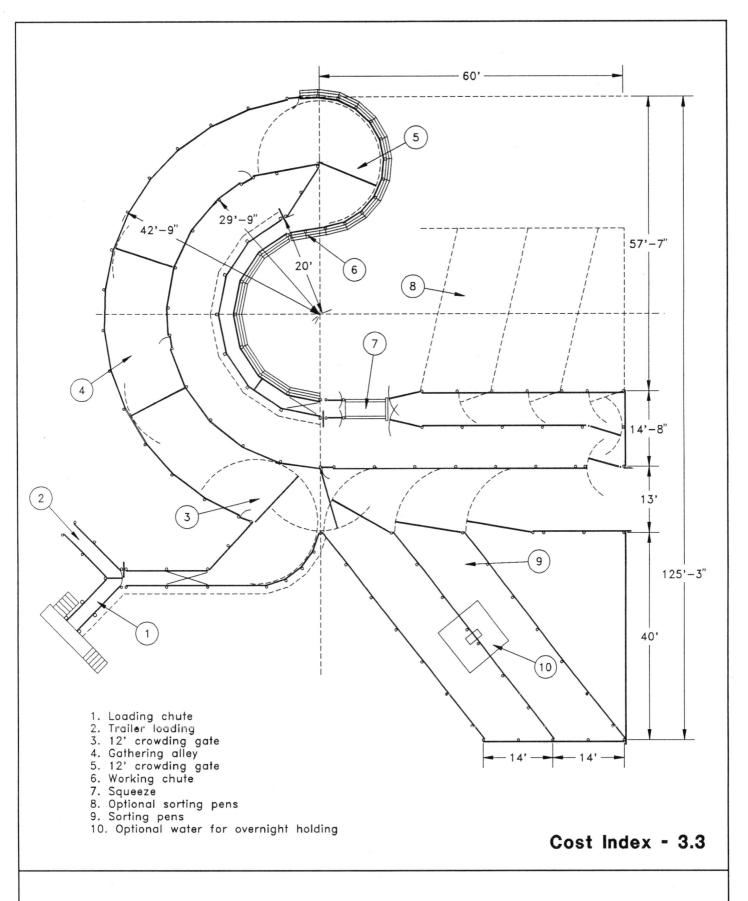

60'

5

42'-9"

29'-9"

20'

6

57'-7"

8

4

7

14'-8"

3

13'

2

9

125'-3"

1

40'

10

1. Loading chute
2. Trailer loading
3. 12' crowding gate
4. Gathering alley
5. 12' crowding gate
6. Working chute
7. Squeeze
8. Optional sorting pens
9. Sorting pens
10. Optional water for overnight holding

14'   14'

Cost Index - 3.3

SASKATCHEWAN S187   **CORRAL LAYOUT 15**

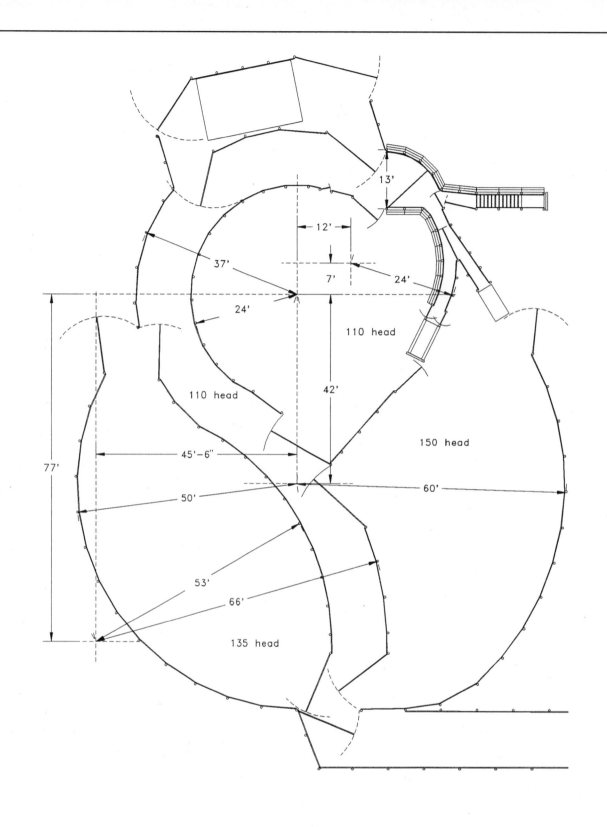

Layout adapted by Wayne Winchell from T. Grandin layout.

GRANDIN/PEMBINA   CORRAL LAYOUT 16

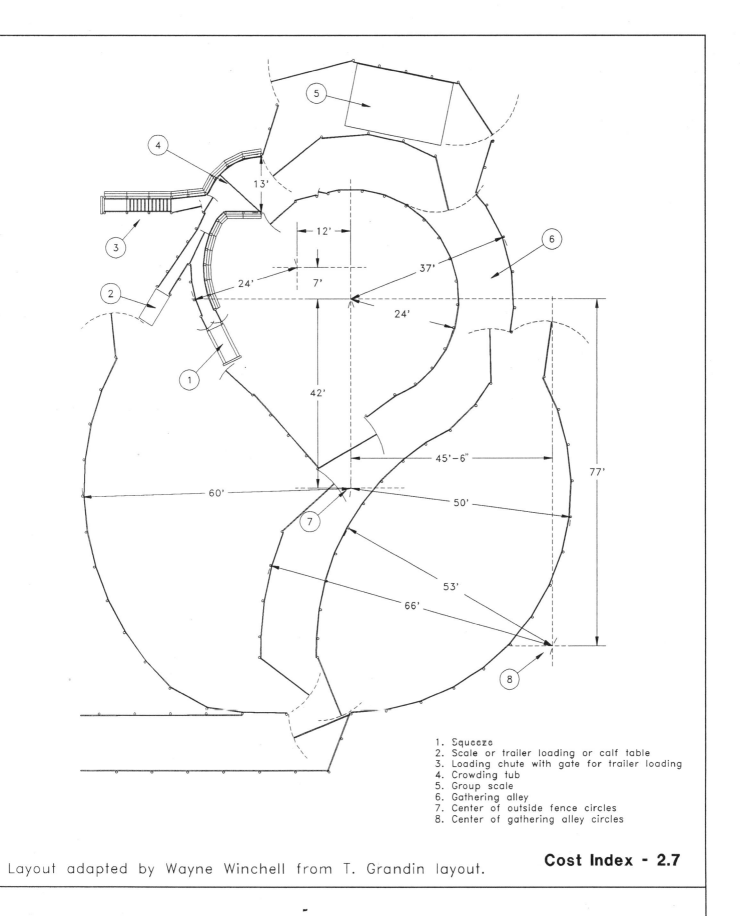

1. Squeeze
2. Scale or trailer loading or calf table
3. Loading chute with gate for trailer loading
4. Crowding tub
5. Group scale
6. Gathering alley
7. Center of outside fence circles
8. Center of gathering alley circles

Layout adapted by Wayne Winchell from T. Grandin layout.

Cost Index - 2.7

GRANDIN/PEMBINA

CORRAL LAYOUT 16

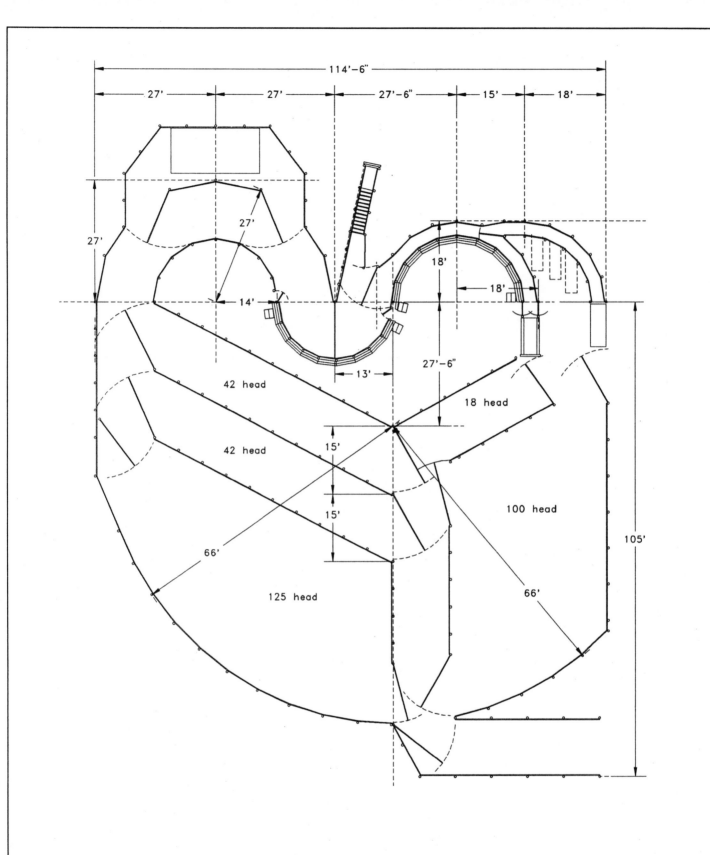

114'−6"

27'   27'   27'−6"   15'   18'

27'

27'

14'

18'

18'

27'−6"

13'

42 head

42 head

18 head

15'

15'

100 head

66'

105'

66'

125 head

Layout adapted from Temple Grandin by Wayne Winchell

GRANDIN/WINCHELL LARGE CORRAL   CORRAL LAYOUT 17

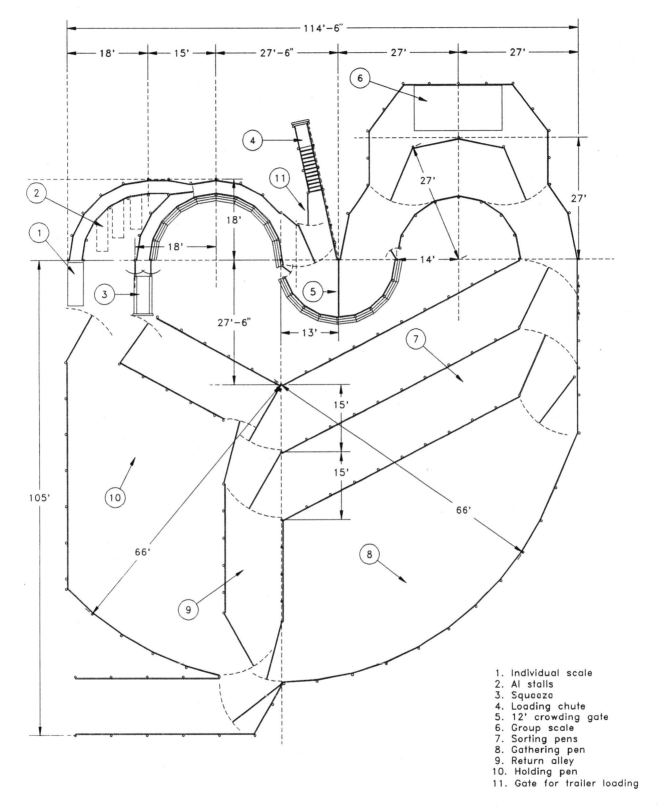

114'-6"

18'   15'   27'-6"   27'   27'

6

4

11

2

1

3

18'

18'

27'

27'

5

14'

27'-6"

13'

7

15'

15'

105'

10

66'

66'

9

8

1. Individual scale
2. AI stalls
3. Squeeze
4. Loading chute
5. 12' crowding gate
6. Group scale
7. Sorting pens
8. Gathering pen
9. Return alley
10. Holding pen
11. Gate for trailer loading

Layout adapted from Temple Grandin by Wayne Winchell

Cost Index - 3.7

GRANDIN/WINCHELL LARGE CORRAL   CORRAL LAYOUT 17

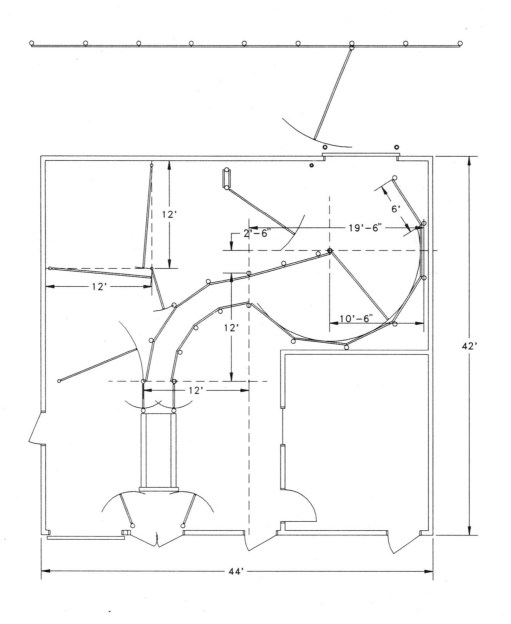

MWPS INDOOR CORRAL   **CORRAL LAYOUT 18**

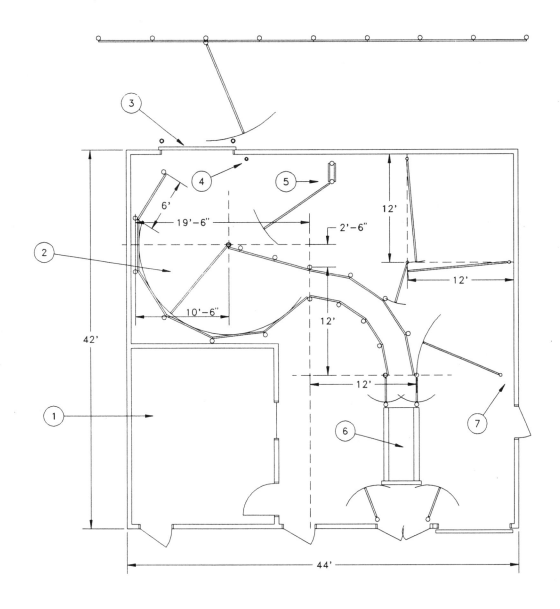

1. Office and supplies
2. 10' crowding gate
3. Sliding door
4. Snub ring
5. Headgate
6. Squeeze
7. Gate with safety pass

Cost Index - 8.3

MWPS INDOOR CORRAL   CORRAL LAYOUT 18

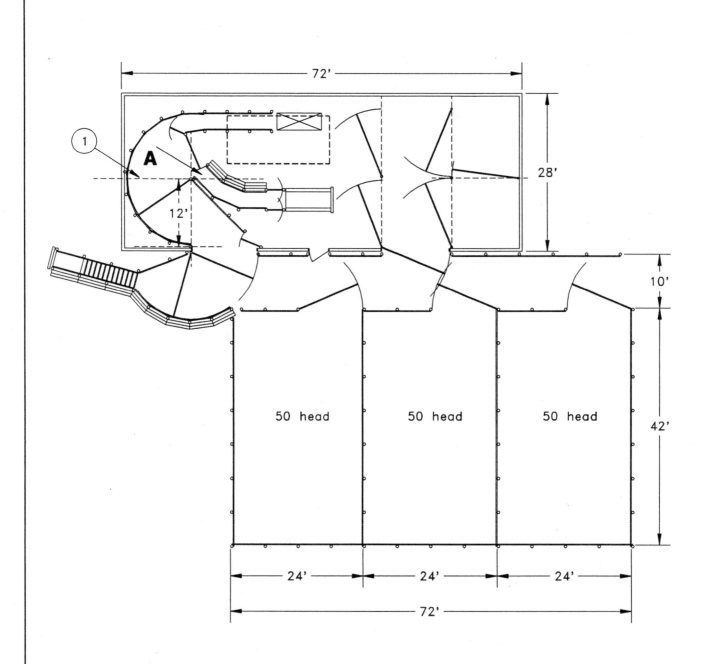

1. T. Grandin has pointed out a potential cattle blocking point
   in this layout.

   A single animal has to be in position A before it can
   see the escape route.

   The plan is a good compromise at fitting a handling system
   into a limited space.

WINCHELL ROOFED PLAN   CORRAL LAYOUT 19

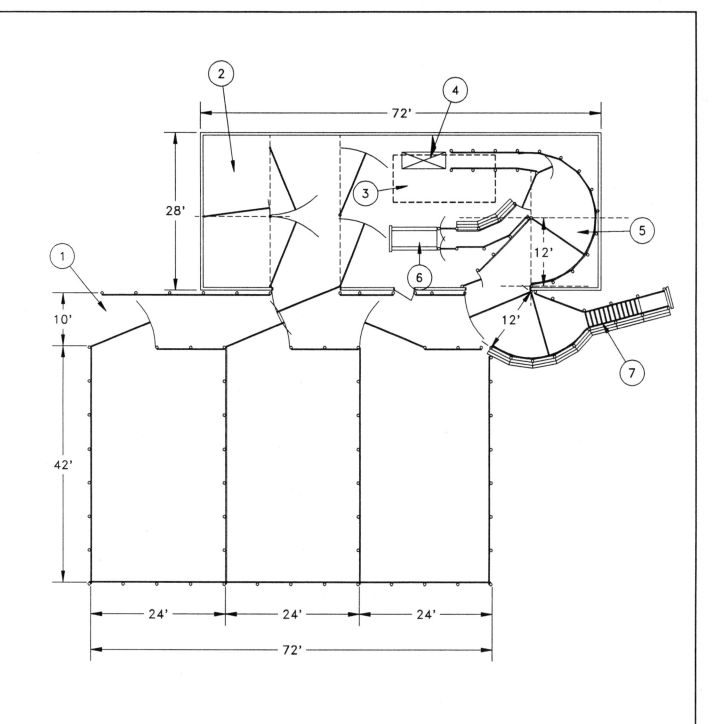

1. From pasture or feedlot
2. Maternity or sick pens
3. Optional group scale
4. Individual scale
5. 12' crowding pen
6. Squeeze
7. Loading chute

Cost Index - 9.5

WINCHELL ROOFED PLAN

CORRAL LAYOUT 19

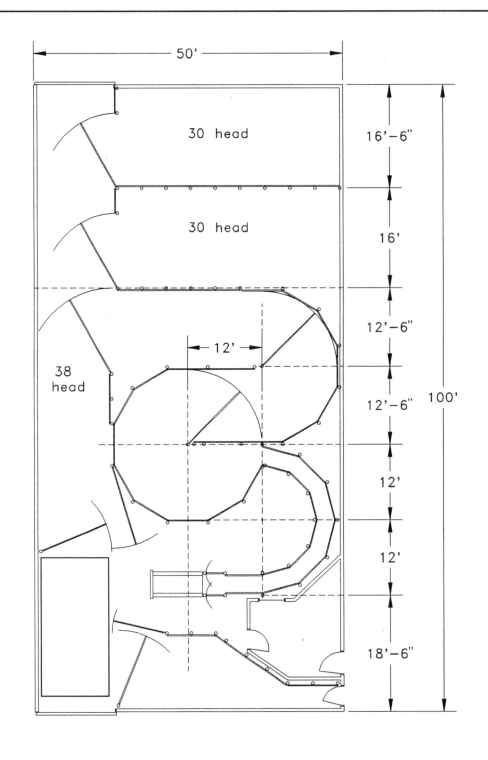

DARBY COVERED CORRAL

CORRAL LAYOUT 20

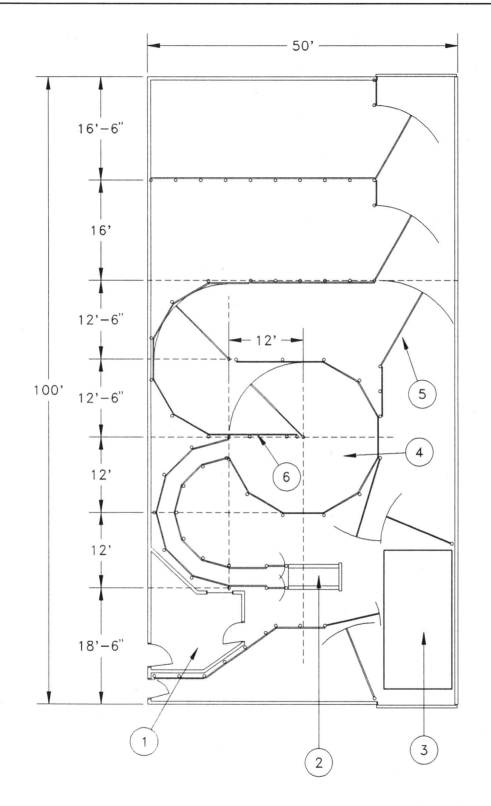

50'

16'-6"

16'

12'-6"

12'-6"

100'

12'-6"

12'

12'

18'-6"

12'

1. Office
2. Squeeze
3. Scale
4. 12' crowding
   pens
5. 12' gates
6. Optional gate

1

2

3

4

5

6

Cost Index - 15.0

DARBY COVERED CORRAL

CORRAL LAYOUT 20

CORRAL
G·E·O·M·E·T·R·Y

The geometry of laying out curved fences, working chutes and crowding tubs is explained in the following diagrams and charts. Use a long tape measure to set out the circles. Anchor the end of the tape with a pin to establish the center point of any arc.

The layouts described here use six inch posts and two inch thick planks. If you wish to use different sizes, modify the geometry.

This chapter includes:
- How to Lay Out a Circular Working Chute
- How to Set the Posts for a Circular Working Chute
- How to Lay Out a Circular Crowding Tub
- How to Lay Out a Circular Crowding Tub
  - Method Two

Figure 42. Typical fence layout

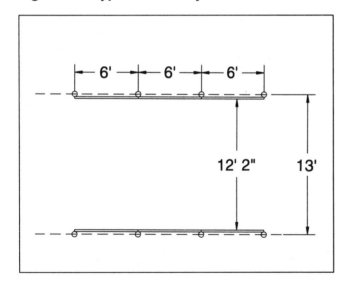

How to Lay Out a Circular Working Chute

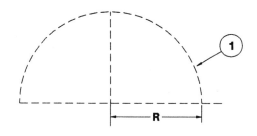

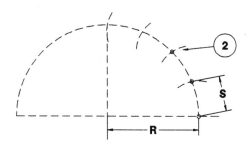

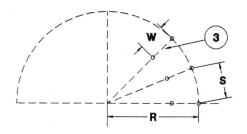

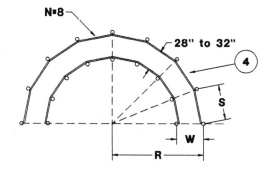

1. Locate the center of the working chute. Draw an arc equal to the chute radius (R).

2. Mark the post locations at distances of S along the arc marking the outside of the chute.

3. The inside posts are located at a distance of W on a line connecting the outside post to the center of the working chute.

4. Cut the planks to length and assemble the working chute.

   The table shows dimensions for various sizes of single file working chutes.

R chute radius	S outside post spacing	N number of sections	W width of post spacing	
			28" chute	32" chute
8'	4' 2"	6	3' 3"	3' 7"
12'	6' 3"	6	3' 3"	3' 7"
	4' 9"	8	3' 3"	3' 7"
16'	6' 3"	8	3' 3"	3' 7"
	4' 2"	12	3' 2"	3' 6"
20'	6' 3"	10	3' 3"	3' 7"
	4' 6"	14	3' 2"	3' 6"
24'	6' 3"	12	3' 2"	3' 7"

Assumptions: 6" posts, 2" planks.

How to Set The Posts for a Circular Working Chute

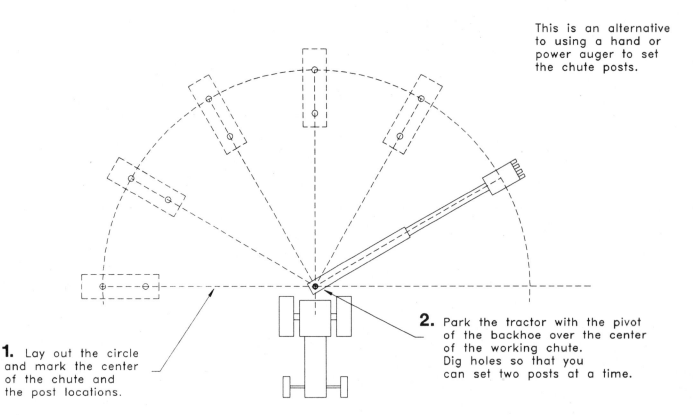

This is an alternative to using a hand or power auger to set the chute posts.

1. Lay out the circle and mark the center of the chute and the post locations.

2. Park the tractor with the pivot of the backhoe over the center of the working chute. Dig holes so that you can set two posts at a time.

3. Build a jig to hold the posts at the correct spacing, allow for the width of the planks. Add 4" for 2" planks.

4. Scabs to hold the posts in position until they are tamped solid. The bottom scab is at the height needed to establish the grade.

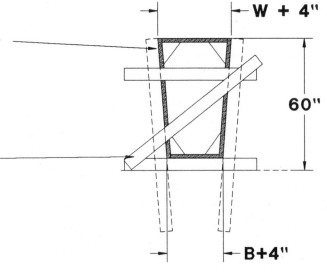

This is a construction method developed by Saskatchewan Agricultural Engineers. See plan S184.

How to Lay Out a Circular Crowding Tub

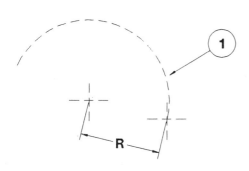

1. Locate the center of the tub. This is the location of the crowding gate hinge post. Draw an arc equal to the crowding tub radius (R).

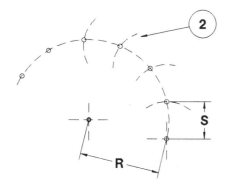

2. Mark the post locations at 4' or 6' distances (S) along the arc.

3. Put in the center post and hang the crowding gate (G). Cut the planks and build the tub walls.

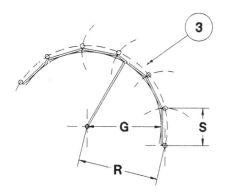

Assumptions: 6" posts, 2" planks.

	G	R
	gate length	tub radius
	8'	8' 8"
Post spacing **S=4'**	**10'**	10' 7"
	12'	12' 7"
	14'	14' 7"
	16'	16' 6"

	G	R
	gate length	tub radius
	8'	8' 11"
Post spacing **S=6'**	**10'**	10' 10"
	12'	12' 9"
	14'	14' 9"
	16'	16' 8"

How to Lay Out a Circular Crowding Tub - Method Two

1. Locate the end posts of the crowding tub. The distance between the posts depends on the number of sections of tub. Read the distance (C) from the table.

Draw arcs equal to the tub radius from each end post. The point where the two arcs intersect is the location of the crowding gate post.

2. Draw an arc with a length equal to the tub radius (R), using the crowding tub post as the center of the arc.

3. Mark the location of the crowding tub posts at 4' intervals along the arc that you just drew using the crowding tub post as a center.

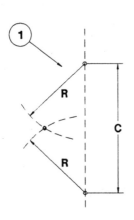

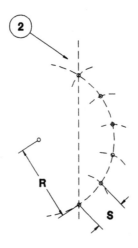

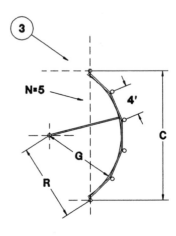

Assumptions: 6" posts, 2" planks, 4' post spacing.

R tub radius	G gate length	C chord length for 3 to 7 sections of crowding tub				
		3	**4**	**5**	**6**	**7**
8'	7' 4"	11'	13' 7"	15' 3"		
8' 6"	7' 10"	11' 1"	13' 10"	15' 9"		
9'	8' 4"	11' 3"	14' 1"	16' 2"	17' 1"	
9' 6"	8' 10"	11' 4"	14' 3"	16' 7"	18' 2"	
10'	9' 5"		14' 5"	16' 11"	18' 8"	
10' 6"	9' 11"		14' 7"	17' 2"	19' 2"	
11'	10' 5"		14' 8"	17' 5"	19' 7"	
11' 6"	10' 11"			17' 7"	19' 11"	21' 8"
12'	11' 5"			17' 10"	20' 3"	22' 1"
12' 6"	11' 11"			18'	20' 6"	22' 7"
13'	12' 5"			18' 2"	20' 9"	22' 11"

CORRAL
C·O·S·T·S

Corral layout 1 will use $1,200 - $1,400 of materials, depending on local costs and construction methods. The table shows relative costs of layouts 2 to 20 as a multiple of layout 1, the minimum working corral. The assumptions used were:

Lumber cost $/1,000 board feet
1x6 rough - 225.00
2x6 rough - 275.00
2x6 planed- 350.00

▶ POSTS

Top size	8 ft.	Length 10 ft.	12 ft.
4 in.	5.00	7.00	
5 in.	6.00	8.00	11.00
6 in.	9.00	12.00	14.00
7 in.	12.00	14.00	18.00
8 in.	14.00	17.00	20.00

These costs were valid January, 1993.

Typical corral fences use six inch top diameter posts, eight feet on centre, with four - 2 x 6 rough planks as rails. The working chutes and crowding tubs are built with solid sides. The cost of a squeeze was not included.

For layouts 18 and 19, uninsulated pole building with an earth floor, $5.50/square foot for materials was assumed. For layout 20, $3.90/square foot was used. Only the building material package cost was used.

Corral layout	Relative cost
1	1
2	1.35
3	1.35
4	2.3
5	2.1
6	2.25
7	1.7
8	2.45
9	2.1
10	2.7
11	2.0
12	2.5
13	2.25
14	3.1
15	3.3
16	2.7
17	3.7
18	8.3
19	9.5
20	15.0

C·O·M·P·O·N·E·N·T·S

To complete the corral design you will make decisions about fence and gate construction and choose from various designs of scales, cattle squeezes, calf tables and A I chutes.

▶ FENCE DESIGN

Most corral fences are five or six feet high with posts set three or four feet into the ground. For Hereford or Angus cattle, five foot fences are okay. For European breeds consider six foot fences.

Use rough lumber, 2 x 6s for strength. Five foot corral fences will have four rails or planks and six foot fences will use five rails. Leave the bottom plank high enough to roll under for a safe escape from the pen.

If fences have cattle on both sides, consider a 2 x 6 guard rail on the opposite side to the four or five regular fence planks. For extra reinforcement, a 2 x 6 placed flat along the top of the posts can stiffen a section of fence.

▶ GATES

Gates can be made of wood or steel. Corner posts for crowding gates are usually made of steel pipe. Fill concrete around the posts. The following drawings show typical gate and latch details.

Figure 43. Fence design

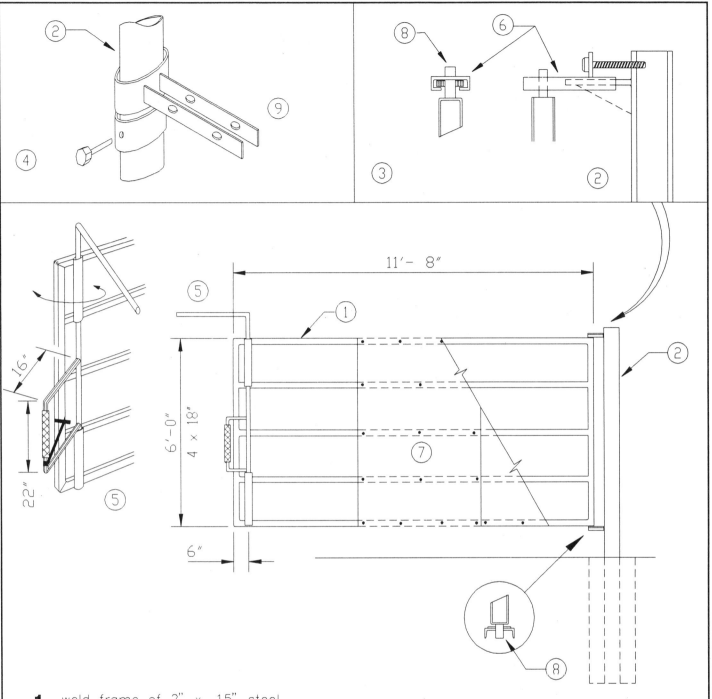

1. weld frame of 2" × .15" steel
2. 6" × .25" steel pipe post in concrete
3. typical hinge for steel gate post
4. pivot detail for a crowding gate
5. ratchet device for a crowding gate
   1.5" pipe, cover bumper with rubber and
   tie back to gate with a rubber strap

6. 3" channel on 0.65" bar with threaded adjusting rod
7. cover front with 19 mm plywood
8. 1" steel pin pivots in ⑤
9. 2" × 20" × .25" steel strap

Crowding Gate 1   - Dennis Darby

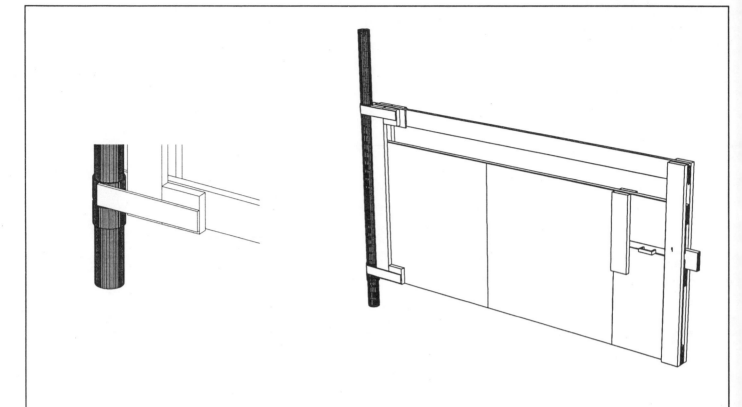

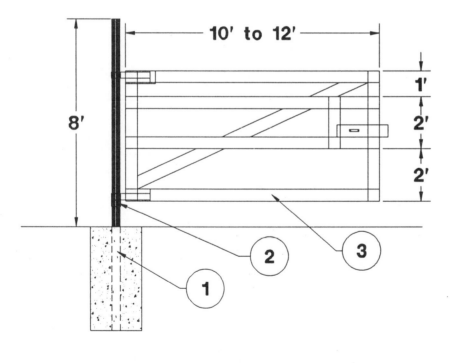

1. Concrete backfill to 4' in soft soils. 3-1/2" diameter steel post, 12' long.

2. 4" steel pipe sleeve bolted to post. Additional holes for height adjustment. The hinge is a 4" pipe up to 8" long with grease fitting tapped into the sleeve. Weld 3/8" x 3" flat iron to form hinge straps.

3. 2x6 rails for framing. The latch board is also a 2x6.

Crowding Gate 2

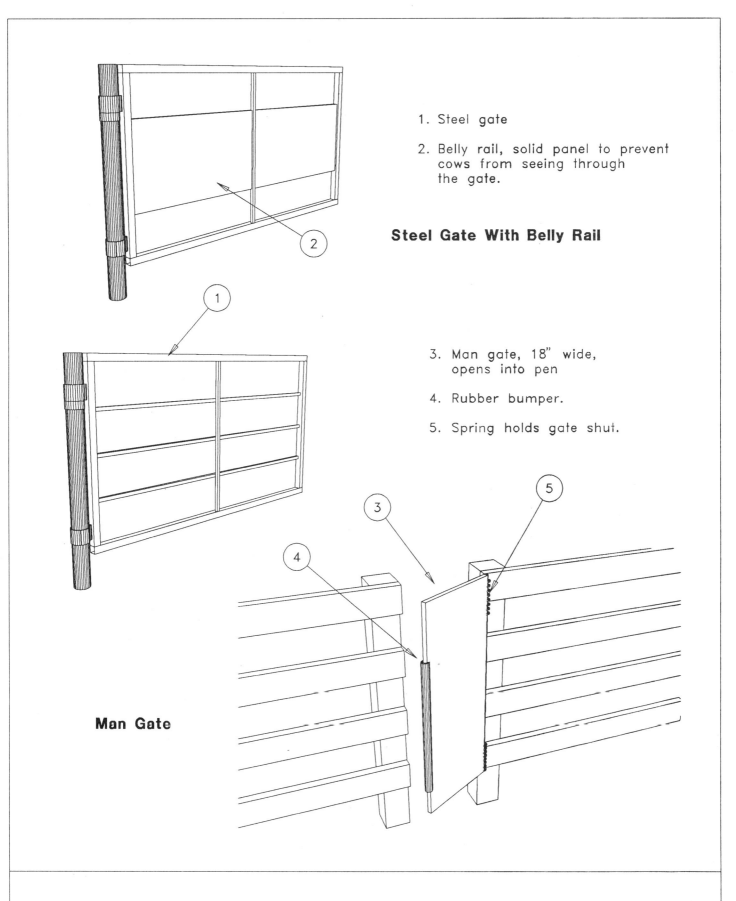

1. Steel gate

2. Belly rail, solid panel to prevent cows from seeing through the gate.

Steel Gate With Belly Rail

3. Man gate, 18" wide, opens into pen

4. Rubber bumper.

5. Spring holds gate shut.

Man Gate

Gate Details 3

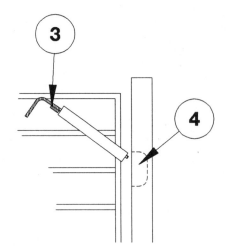

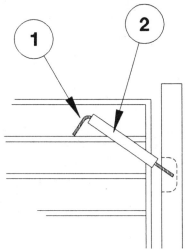

1. 1" steel rod
2. 30" steel sleeve
3. Tab to hold latch open
4. Slot in post to allow gate movement

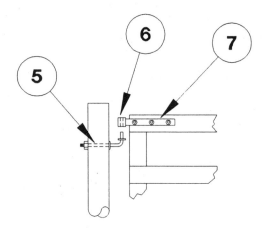

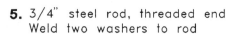

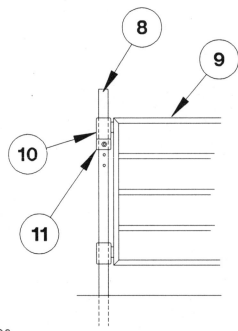

5. 3/4" steel rod, threaded end
   Weld two washers to rod
6. Pipe section to fit over rod
7. Weld two steel straps to pipe section
   and bolt to wood gate

8. 3-1/2" steel pipe
9. Steel gate. Weld a 1" spacer to the gate,
   then weld spacer to hinge pipe.
10. 4" x 8" steel pipe sleeve rotates on the post,
    thread in grease fittings.
11. 4" x 4" collar bolted to post. Extra hole for height adjustment.

Fence, Latch Details 1

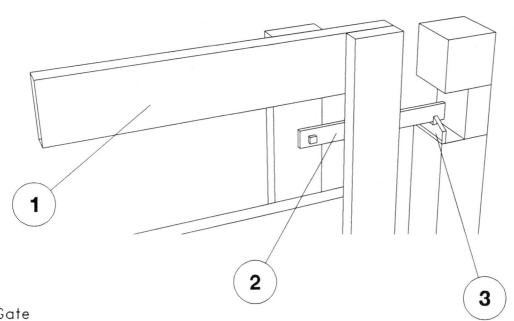

1. Gate
2. Spring loaded strap iron.
3. 1/4" steel plate, self latching
4. Gate
5. Slide stick latch

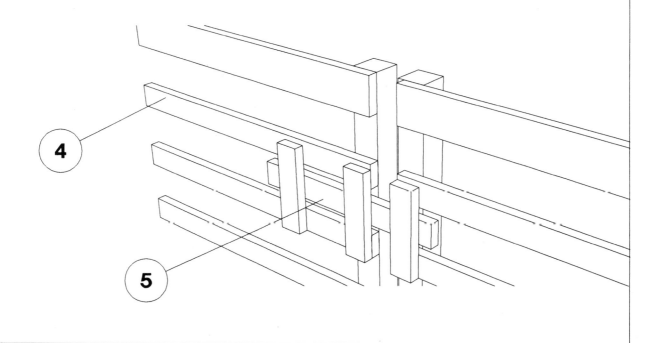

Latch Details 2

▶ SQUEEZE SELECTION

A headgate and/or squeeze to restrain cattle is an essential tool for herd health care. It is less stressful for animals to be held snugly in a squeeze than to be moving about. The important features to consider when choosing a squeeze are headgate design, squeeze geometry, floor, palpation gates, hydraulic or manual operation, removable or swing away panels for access and cattle and operator safety.

▶ HEADGATES

Two choices are straight bars or curved bars. Straight bars are safer because cows are less likely to choke if they go down. The disadvantage of straight bars is that cattle can move their head up and down.

The three most common types of headgates are:

Self Catching
The headgate doors are vertical double doors. To open they swing into the squeeze. As the cow's shoulders hit the door and the operator swings the door shut, the cow is trapped in the headgate. Be sure that the width is adjustable. Sometimes the cattle can back up, throw the gate open and escape.

Scissor or Stanchion
These headgate doors are hinged at the bottom, they swing together to hold the animal, swing apart to release it.

Full Opening Stanchion
The doors move on tracks from a closed to open position.

All three types of headgates are available with curved or straight bars.

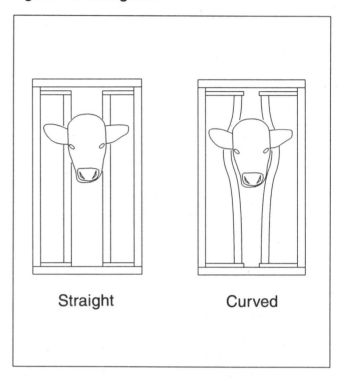

Figure 44. Headgates

Straight   Curved

	Self Catching	Scissor Stanchion	Full Opening
Use this gate for:	Gentle cattle with no horns.	General purpose, large feedlots, adjustable for cattle of mixed sizes	General purpose, mixed sizes as the gate seldom needs adjustment, large bulls can easily exit.
Don't use this gate for:	Wild cattle, horned cattle, mixed sized groups (gate needs adjustment for different sizes), large feedlots.	Large bulls, (they have trouble stepping out through the narrow space at the bottom of the gate).	Big, wild cattle, large feedlots, (many of these gates are not strong enough for constant heavy use).
Be careful!	Carefully maintain the mechanism. Also, head and shoulder injuries are possible if the animals slam into the gate.	Don't catch the animals' legs or knees in the gate and cause injuries.	Maintain the mechanism to prevent jamming. Don't let an excited animal trip over the bottom track.

Figure 45. Types of headgates

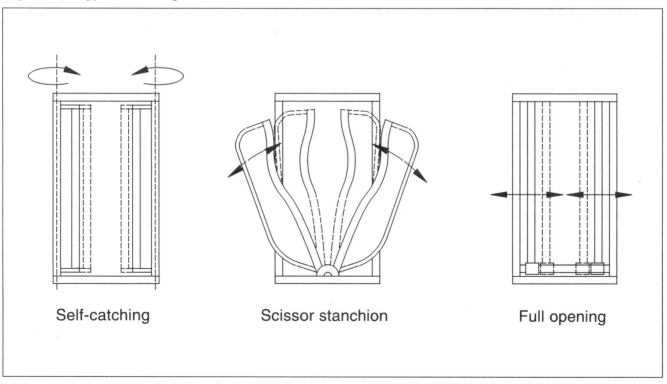

Self-catching   Scissor stanchion   Full opening

▶ SQUEEZE CHUTE GEOMETRY

The squeeze chute sides should move in and out together so that the cattle are not thrown off balance. Squeezes can have verticial or 'V' shaped sides. 'V' shaped sides support the cattle to prevent them from going down and choking.

Adjust the inside width at the bottom of a 'V' shaped squeeze to fit the cattle.

- six inches for 250 - 400 lb. calves.
- eight inches for 600 - 800 lb. cattle.
- 12 inches for heavy feeders and cows.
- 14 inches to 16 inches for larger bulls.

A hydraulically operated mechanism for adjusting the width is a big advantage here. Mechnical adjustments tend not to be used.

▶ HYDRAULIC OR MECHANICAL?

A well designed hydraulic squeeze takes less effort to use, is faster, sturdier and is safer for the operator and animal than a manually operated squeeze. A hydraulic squeeze can be $5,000 - $8,000 while a manual squeeze is around $1,800 (Cattlemen magazine,1992).

Be careful with relief pressure settings so cattle don't get injured. If cattle are held for long periods, release some squeeze pressure.

Disadvantages of hydraulic squeezes are:

- Noise - cattle can hear high frequencies similar to dogs. Move the noisy pump and motor well away from the squeeze, buy longer hoses.

- There is no side release, the cattle have to go out the front or back.

- May injure cattle when used by inexperienced operators.

▶ PALPATION OR VET GATES

These gates swing back against the working chute to allow access to the rear of the cattle. Strong doors and good latches are important. Solid gates prevent cattle in the working chute from seeing the squeeze.

▶ HEAD BASKET

A head basket or gate made of 3/4 inch steel rod will hold the animal inside the squeeze and act as a visual barrier.

. Cattle will slow down, so you don't have to slam the headgate shut, an advantage for a one person operation. For vaccinating and warble treatment, you don't even need the headgate.

Figure 46. Head basket - open

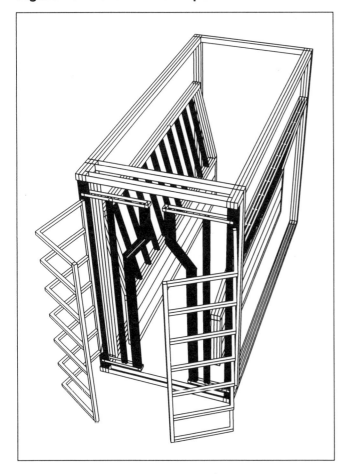

▶ FLOOR

Cattle need a non-slip floor to give them secure footing. Floors in commercial squeezes are made of wood, steel or concrete. Wood and steel can be slippery. Wood is less durable, steel is noisy and concrete is heavy. For any floor, check for grooves or slats that give cattle good footing. The distance between grooves in a floor should be small enough so that a cow's hoof will always contact a groove.

Figure 47. Head basket - closed

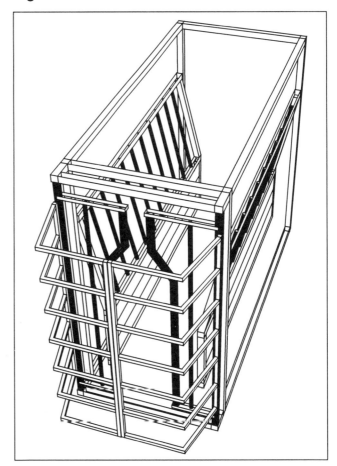

▶ BLIND BOX

An old idea is using a box with solid sides, a headgate on the front and vet gates at the rear. Cattle handle quietly as they cannot see you intruding their flight zone. Doors on the side and a drop panel along the bottom allow you full access to the animal. Build your own blind box with rough planks. Recommended inside dimensions are: length 8'6", height 6'6", width 30".

Figure 48. Blind box

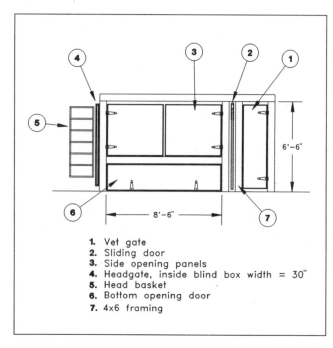

1. Vet gate
2. Sliding door
3. Side opening panels
4. Headgate, inside blind box width = 30"
5. Head basket
6. Bottom opening door
7. 4x6 framing

▶ SAFETY

Levers on manually operated headgates can be dangerous. Buy a gate or modify it so that levers cannot drop on your head or fly up and strike you.

Animals that run wildly into a chute and crash against a headgate can seriously injure their necks and shoulders. Neck extenders on headgates can easily injure an animal's jaw. With a hydraulic chute, slow the cattle down with the squeeze before they reach the headgate. Operators who handle deer or elk routinely add padding to their equipment.

▶ REWARDS

Stress depends on previous experience. For small herds, train cattle by letting them pass through an open squeeze chute and give them some grain. Repeat until the cows voluntarily enter the squeeze chute. The first experience with a squeeze shouldn't be painful. Quiet handling is important.

▶ CALF TABLES

Calf tables are small squeezes that can tilt and restrain calves in a prone position. The operator can work on the animal in a safe position.

The table can be located off the main working chute.

▶ A. I. CHUTE

Hold cows in a 'dark box' for artificial insemination (A.I.). The cows will stand quietly and can be easily restrained. Improved conception rates result from gentle handling.

The dark box is solid on the sides, top and front. The cow is restrained from behind. After insemination the cow leaves from a front gate.

Figure 49. Pregnancy testing and A.I. chute

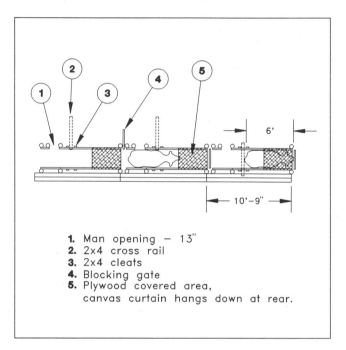

1. Man opening — 13"
2. 2x4 cross rail
3. 2x4 cleats
4. Blocking gate
5. Plywood covered area, canvas curtain hangs down at rear.

▶ SCALES

Cattle scales are an important marketing tool, either to weigh cattle individually or as a group on a platform. A single scale can determine the rate of gain or be used as a selection tool or to check on the health of bred cows. Group scales can weigh groups of cattle, bales, feed wagons, grain or trucks.

Single scales can have their own frame or cage for holding an animal or can be mounted in the form of load cells under a conventional cattle squeeze.

Group scales also need a cage to hold the cattle.

Typical costs for group scales are:
      10' x 12' $ 7,500 - $10,000
      10' x 20' $ 9,500 - $12,000
      10' x 30' $11,500 - $15,000

Most group scales use electronic load cells and do not require pits.

Figure 50. Herringbone A.I. breeding chute

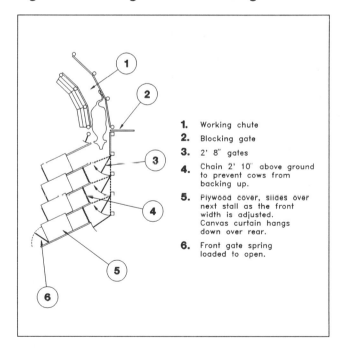

1. Working chute
2. Blocking gate
3. 2' 8" gates
4. Chain 2' 10" above ground to prevent cows from backing up.
5. Plywood cover, slides over next stall as the front width is adjusted. Canvas curtain hangs down over rear.
6. Front gate spring loaded to open.

Typical individual scales mounted under cattle squeezes cost $1,900 - $2,000. Mobile squeezes with their own cage may be $2,500 -$5,000 (see PAMI Report 654)

► TYPES OF SCALES

Mechanical Scales
- Use a balance beam, are simple and durable.
- Don't require external power.
- May need calibration every 50 cattle.

Hydraulic Load Cell Scales
- Suspend the cage from a hydraulic load cell and measure the weight with a pressure gauge.
- Quick, easy, no electricity needed.
- Be careful about the stability of the floor system, cattle may fall and be unnerved.
- Recalibrate after 20 cattle.

Electronic Scales
- Easy to use, fast.
- Require power supply or batteries.

Protect the electronics from the harsh environment. Mount load cells up high, out of the moisture if possible.
- Re-zero the scale every 15 cattle or so.

Most companies will sell an electronic monitor legal for trade. If you want an electronic scale that is legal for trade, check with Canadian Consumer and Corporate Affairs, Weights and Measures Device Inspections, for certification.

R·E·F·E·R·E·N·C·E·S

► **PLANS AND PUBLICATIONS**
A. Canada Plan Service (January, 1992)

Beef Cattle Housing & Equipment

Number Plan Title
*1000 Beef Cattle Housing & Equipment
 1303 Calving Barn
*M1351 Calf Range Shelter (Rigid Frame)
*1352 Calf Range Shelter (Open Front)
*1353 Portable Pipe Frame Calving Shelter
 1453 Western Feedlot for South Facing Slope
 1454 Western Feedlot for Diagonal Slope
*1480 Fenceline Feeder (Wood)
*1486 Fenceline Feeder (Pipe Frame)
 1611 Portable Calf Creep Feeder
*1621 Covered Concrete Feed Bunk
*1622 Bunk Feed Cart
*1623 Expandable Feed Bunk
*Q1641 Two-Wire Electric Bale Feeding
*1642 Giant Bale Feeder (Steel)
*1643 Giant Bale Feeder (Wood)
*1645 Movable Feed Gates
*1646 Portable Hay Feeder
*M1647 Weathervane Mineral Feeder
*1649 Grain Self-Feeder
*1651 Chopped Hay Feeder for Cattle
*1800 Cattle Handling Facilities (Planning Guide)
*1811 Corral and Feedlot Fencing
*1812 Crowding Gate
*1813 Working Chute
*1814 Blocking Gate
*1816 Stationary Adjustable Loading Chute
*1817 Portable Adjustable Loading Chute
*1818 Pregnancy Testing and A.I. Chute
*1819 Herringbone A.I. Breeding Chute
*1831 Minimum Working Corral
*1832 Small Working Corral
*1833 Cattle Handling Corral
*1834 Corral for Cow- Calf Operations
*1835 Large Working Corral
 (See 8161, 8162 and 8163 for Pole Shed plans)

B. Beef Housing and Equipment Handbook MWPS- 6, Midwest Plan Service

C. Saskatchewan Agriculture
Beef Cattle Handling Facilities 1992.
One Way Gates For Solid Sided Working Chutes,
 Plan S-182.
Working Chute Cross Sections.
Curved Working Chute with Sorting Pens,
 Plan S-185.
Tight-Curved Working Chute - Plan S-186
Semi- Circular Crowding Alley and Working Chute,
 Plan S-187.
The Saskatchewan plans are available in three-dimensional drawings as well as conventional blue prints.

D. Cattle Handling Facilities,
compiled by Wayne Winchell, regional engineer, Alberta Agriculture, Food and Rural Development, Barrhead.

E. Cattle Corrals:
Cow Calf Handling Facilities and Equipment, 1977 WRAES, (Washington, U.S.A.)

F. Canadian Farm Buildings Handbook,
Publication 1822E, 1988, Agriculture Canada.

G. PAMI Report 654, Livestock Scales.

H. Corral Fence Costs,
Lotus 1-2-3 Spreadsheet, Dennis Darby, farm structures engineer, Lethbridge.

M Designates a Metric Plan

*This Leaflet is the complete plan